# Deutsch Aktuell 1

## FIFTH EDITION

## WORKBOOK

**Wolfgang S. Kraft**

Consultant: Hans J. König

EMC/Paradigm Publishing, St. Paul, Minnesota

The publisher would like to thank the following sources for granting permission to reproduce certain material on the pages indicated:

*Austrian National Tourist Office (New York):* 138
*Bayern Tourism:* 39
*Deutsche Telekom:* 22
*Deutsche Bahn:* 170, 172
*Deutsche Bundesliga:* 35, 159
*Deutsche Post:* 21
*Deutscher Wetterdienst:* 66, 71
*Deutsches Jugendherbergswerk:* 16
*Fremdenverkehrsverband München-Oberbayern e.V.:* 119, 176
*Fremdenverkehrsverband Thüringer Wald e.V.:* 174
*Fremdenverkehrsverein Nordrhein-Westfalen e.V.:* 154
*German National Tourist Office (New York):* 146, 182
*German Information Center (New York):* 61
*Hessen Touristik Service e.V.:* 198
*Hohenzollern-Gymnasium Sigmaringen:* 59
*Informationszentrum Naturpark Altmühltal:* 107
*Mannheimer Kongress-und Touristik GmbH:* 136
*Quelle AG:* 122
*Tourismus-Marketing Brandenburg GmbH:* 98
*Tourismusverband Weserbergland-Mittelweser e.V.:* 130
*Tourismusverband Salzburger Land:* 190
*Tourist Information Klingenthal:* 196
*Tourist-Information, Miltenberg am Main:* 79
*Tourist-Information Oberes Maintal-Coburger Land:* 132
*Touristenzentrale Sauerland:* 3, 155
*Verkehrsamt Markneukirchen:* 186
*Verkehrsverein Aachen e.V.:* 85
*Verkehrsverein für Flensburg und Umgebung e.V.:* 100, 114
*Verkehrsverein Luzern:* 28
*Waldinger, Karl-Georg:* 143
*Wirtschaftsförderung und Tourismus GmbH im Mainz-Kinzig-Kreis:* 52

ISBN-13 978-0-82192-539-3
ISBN-10 0-8219-2539-3

**Published by EMC/Paradigm Publishing**
875 Montreal Way
St. Paul, Minnesota 55102
800-328-1452
www.emcp.com
E-mail: educate@emcp.com

Printed in the United States of America
   13 14 XXX      10 11

# KAPITEL 1

## Lektion A

**1** Look at the illustration and write in the bubbles what these people might be saying to each other.

## 2 Wer ist das? Look at the newspaper announcements and write the name or names of the people described. This person/these people...

**Petra 30**

Die zwanzig, die sind längst vorbei,
erlebt hast Du so Allerlei.

Bleib weiter wie Dich jeder kennt, mit Deinem Schwung und
Temperament. Spielt das Wetter am Samstag auch nicht mit, egal -
wir kennen das - dies macht uns nichts.

Wir wünschen Dir das Allerbeste zum 30. Geburtstagsfeste.

*Andreas, Katharina, Ralf, Birgit, Jochen, Monika,
Dominik, David, Elisa, Anna-Maria und Michelle*

**Mario Kaluza
Jutta Zarschizky**

geb. Müller

Die standesamtliche Trauung ist
um 11.30 Uhr im Amtshaus Brilon.

**Anneliese wird 60 !**

60 Jahre sind verronnen,
seid Du auf die Welt gekommen.
60 Jahre? Ach, welch ein Schreck,
die Jugend und der Lack sind weg.
Die Knochen knacken, Muskeln schmerzen.
Doch das eine sollst Du wissen,
ohne Dich wären wir aufgeschmissen.
Für alles was Du tust, hab Dank,
bleib gesund und wird' nicht krank.
Wir wünschen Dir zu Deinem Feste,
Gesundheit, Glück und viele Gäste.

**Peter, Angie und Marie**

Von Madfeld aus dem Sauerland
klingt's „Vivat" hoch zum Nordseestrand.

Dort kommt der Gruß bei **Leon** an,

**1 Jahr** alt wird der kleine Mann.

Die herzlichsten Glückwünsche an **unseren Leon** senden
Opa Bernd, Oma Brigitte, Patenonkel Sascha
sowie Fritz und Paul

*Danke*
für die vielen Glückwünsche und
Geschenke zu meinem 80. Geburtstag.
Mein besonderer Dank gilt meiner Frau,
meiner Familie, meinen Freunden,
den Nachbarn und Rat der der Stadt.
Danke dem Sportverein, Schützenverein,
Verkehrsverein und SGV.
Ich habe mich sehr über Euer Kommen gefreut.

Danke auch für die vielen
Genesungswünsche während meines
Krankenhaus- und Reha-Aufenthaltes.
Sie haben mir viel Kraft gegeben.

*Karl Frigger*

## Lieber Papa!

Wir möchten Dir herzlich zu Deinem

### 65. Geburtstag

gratulieren und einfach Danke sagen,
dass Du immer für uns da bist.

**Deine Kinder
Sigrid, Heide und Jörg**

1. are getting married.

   _____

2. are sending a congratulatory message for her 60th birthday.

   _____

3. is celebrating her 30th birthday.

   _____

4. is thanking several people for coming to his 80th birthday celebration.

   _____

5. had the name of Müller as her maiden name.

   _____

6. are congratulating their father on his birthday.

   _____

7. are wishing her well on her 30th birthday and are female. Name them.

   _____

8. is one year old.

   _____

## 3 *Wie heißt er oder sie?* Write a complete answer to this question using the names from the illustration.

*Beispiel:*

Vanessa
Sie heißt Vanessa.

1.  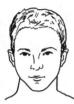 Florian

_____

2.   Karsten

_____

3.   Birgit

_____

4.   Carmen

_____

5.   Timo

_____

6.   Dagmar

_____

## 4 Match the German words with the English descriptions. You will not need all the German phrases provided.

_____ 1. normal greeting

_____ 2. greeting in the morning

_____ 3. "good-bye" that means "hope to see you again"

_____ 4. young people greeting each other in southern Germany

_____ 5. Austrians greeting each other

_____ 6. a greeting that is not too different from our "Hi!"

_____ 7. a normal but mumbled evening greeting

_____ 8. tourists often see this greeting on a sign as they drive into a German town

_____ 9. a greeting commonly heard around 7 P.M.

A. Auf Wiedersehen!

B. Willkommen!

C. Guten Abend!

D. Tschüs!

E. Grüß dich!

F. N' Abend!

G. Sehr nett!

H. Guten Tag!

I. Guten Morgen!

J. Wirklich!

K. Servus!

L. Hallo!

## 5 Write the problem and solution in German.

*Beispiel:* 1 + 4 = ?
Eins plus vier ist fünf.

1. 5 + 7 = ?

_____

2. 3 + 6 = ?

_____

3. 4 + 13 = ?

_____

4. 10 + 8 = ?

_____

5. 11 + 9 = ?

_____

**6** **Beantworte diese Fragen!** (Answer these questions!) Write a complete sentence for each answer.

1. Wie heißt du?

   _____

2. Wie alt bist du?

   _____

3. Wie heißt dein Freund oder deine Freundin?

   _____

4. Wie geht's?

   _____

5. Woher kommst du?

   _____

6. Wer ist das?

   _____

# KAPITEL 1

## Lektion B

**7** Fill in the appropriate words. The first letters, when read in sequence, spell a German greeting.

1. WIE GEHT ES IHNEN? SEHR _____.

2. KENNST DU KLAUS _____ PETER?

3. TSCHAU ODER _____ HEISST *AUF WIEDERSEHEN*.

4. ICH KENNE ROLF. _____ IST SECHZEHN.

5. KENNST DU TINA? JA, SIE IST SEHR _____.

6. GUTEN _____, HERR SCHMIDT!

7. WIE _____ IST GISELA? FÜNFZEHN.

8. ER WOHNT _____ UM DIE ECKE.

**8** Match the sentences on the left with those on the right. Each pair will become a conversational exchange.

_____ 1. Susanne wohnt da. Und Tina?

_____ 2. Ist Tanja hier?

_____ 3. Alex ist dein Freund?

_____ 4. Wo wohnst du?

_____ 5. Wie geht's?

_____ 6. Wohnt sie gleich um die Ecke?

A. Nein, fünfzehn Minuten von hier.

B. Ich wohne nicht weit von hier.

C. Nicht sehr gut.

D. Nein, sie ist da drüben.

E. Sie wohnt auch da.

F. Nein, Boris.

**9** Fill in the missing words.

1. Kennst _____ Angelika gut?

2. Wo wohnen _____, Herr Baumann?

3. Ich habe eine _____. Sie heißt Petra.

4. Wie _____ es Ihnen?

5. _____ heißt Walter.

6. _____ dich, Steffie!

7. Mein Freund _____ nur drei Minuten von hier.

8. Guten _____, Frau Krause!

9. _____ geht's? Nicht schlecht.

10. Wie _____ ist Uli? Sechzehn.

## 10 Indicate whether you would use *du* or *Sie* in the following situations. Write in your answers.

1. Brothers and sisters address each other with _____.

2. Two adults are being introduced to each other. Both address each other with _____.

3. Among each other, young people use _____.

4. In prayers and church services people address God as _____.

5. Military comrades address each other with _____.

6. Adult acquaintances address each other with _____.

7. Friends call each other _____.

8. People talking to animals use _____.

9. Adults talking to children use _____.

10. Most colleagues in an office use _____.

## 11 Form complete sentences by writing the words in the correct order. Capitalize words as needed.

*Beispiel:*  Ecke / Christine / die / wohnt / um / gleich
Christine wohnt gleich um die Ecke.

1. wohne / da / ich / drüben

   _____

2. deine / Freundin / wo / ist

   _____

3. Tag / Gruber / Guten / Herr

   _____

4. Bernd / geht's / wie

   _____

5. Frau / auf / Dietrich / Wiedersehen

   _____

6. ist / Tina / alt / wie

_____

7. kommen / Frau / woher / Schulz / Sie

_____

8. du / Pauls / Freundin / kennst

_____

## 12 Fill in the appropriate verb form for each sentence.

1. (kennen) Ich _____ das Mädchen nicht.

2. (gehen) Wie _____ es Ihnen, Frau Braun?

3. (sein) Wie alt _____ du, Rudi?

4. (kennen) _____ du Susanne gut?

5. (wohnen) _____ Sie weit von hier?

6. (heißen) Der Junge _____ Daniel.

7. (wohnen) Wo _____ ihr?

8. (sein) Ich _____ vierzehn.

## 13 Write the appropriate verb endings.

1. Wie heiß _____ du?

2. Ich heiß _____ Katrin.

3. Wo wohn _____ ihr, Angelika und Monika?

4. Wir wohn _____ in der Stadt.

5. Kenn _____ Sie Frau Hocker?

6. Ja, ich kenn _____ sie sehr gut.

7. Wie geh _____ es Dieter?

8. Gut. Geh _____ es Günter schlecht?

**14** **Develop a short conversation based on the illustration. Write at least five sentences.**

_____

_____

_____

_____

_____

_____

_____

_____

_____

_____

**15** **Fill out the form below. Can you figure out what these words mean? Except for *Druckbuchstaben* (block letters), *Alter* (age) and *Postleitzahl* (zip code) you should be able to identify the other words, most of which are also listed in the vocabulary at the end of the textbook.**

---

*Bitte mit Druckbuchstaben schreiben:*

Name _____

Vorname_____

Geburtstag _____

Alter_____

Straße/Hausnummer_____

Postleitzahl/Stadt _____

Land _____

Telefon _____

---

**16** **Write a short essay in English about some of the social differences between Germany and the United States. Include such items as greetings, introductions and the usage of *du* versus *Sie*.**

_____

_____

_____

_____

_____

_____

_____

_____

_____

_____

_____

_____

_____

_____

_____

_____

## 17 Kreuzworträtsel (Note: ß = SS)

**WAAGERECHT**

1. Wie ist er? Ganz ___.
3. Robert ist ein ___.
5. ___ kommt Michael? Aus Regensburg.
7. Herr Rickert wohnt nur fünf ___ von hier.
8. ___ geht's?
12. Ich ___ nicht weit von hier.
13. Wie ___ er? Ralf.
14. Ist Petra deine ___?

**SENKRECHT**

1. Kennen Sie Wolf? Nein, er ist ___ hier.
2. Guten ___!
4. Kennst du Monika? ___.
5. Auf ___!
6. Angelika wohnt gleich um die ___.
9. Acht ___ zwei ist zehn.
10. ___ du sechzehn?
11. Wie geht es ___, Frau Hoffmann?
12. ___ ist das? Anne.

# KAPITEL 2

## Lektion A

**1** **Your friend is talking to you. Complete your part of the dialog.**

Du:      Grüß dich!

*Freund:* _____

Du:      Kennst du Rainer?

*Freund:* _____

Du:      Ist er dein Freund?

*Freund:* _____

Du:      Dein Cousin? Wie alt ist er?

*Freund:* _____

Du:      Ist er zu Hause?

*Freund:* _____

Du:      Wo ist er denn?

*Freund:* _____

**2** *Die Familie.* **Fill in the correct relationship word, using the family tree provided.**

**Herr Feil**
**Großvater**

**Frau Feil**
**Großmutter**

**Heiko**

**Herr Hocker**
**Vater**

**Frau Hocker**
**Mutter**

**Bianca**

1. Heiko ist Biancas _____.

2. Frau Hockers Schwester ist Heikos und Biancas _____.

3. Herr Feil ist Frau Hockers _____.

4. Biancas Großmutter heißt _____.

5. Biancas Vater heißt _____.

6. Heiko ist Herr und Frau Hockers _____.

7. Herr und Frau Hocker sind Heikos und Biancas _____.

8. Frau Feil ist Heikos _____.

9. Frau Feil ist Frau Hockers _____.

10. Bianca ist Heikos _____.

Name _____ Datum _____

**3** Write the correct words or names based on the descriptions. You may want to refer to the family tree illustration in the textbook on page 34. Write each word or name in capital letters. The first letters, when read in sequence, spell something that you will need when calling someone.

1. Christa Elstner ist Daniels _____.

2. Herr und Frau Elstner sind Susannes _____.

3. „Wohnen" auf Englisch: _____

4. Daniels Vater heißt Rudi _____.

5. Rudi, Ingrid, Daniel und Susanne sind eine _____.

6. Helga Vogt ist Susannes _____.

7. Ist Christa Elstner Daniels Mutter? _____.

8. Alexandra ist _____ Rudis Schwester.

9. Harald _____ Helga Vogt sind Susannes und Daniels Opa und Oma.

10. Ingrid Elstner ist Susannes _____.

11. Susanne ist ein _____. Susannes Bruder ist ein Junge.

12. Ingrid Elstners _____ heißen Helga und Harald.

13. _____ Elstner ist Daniels Vater.

**4** Write the correct question words—*Wie, Wo, Woher, Wer, Wie viel*—in the blanks.

1. _____ kommst du? Aus Hamburg.

2. _____ wohnen Sie? In Bremen.

3. _____ ist elf plus acht?

4. _____ wohnen Dieters Eltern?

5. _____ heißt sie?

6. _____ ist das? Katjas Bruder.

7. _____ ist das denn? Giselas Freund.

8. _____ ist hier ein Telefon?

9. _____ alt ist sie?

10. _____ kommt da?

**5** *Wo ist das Jugendgästehaus?* **Look over the description about the youth hostel and then answer the questions.**

### Weimar
**Jugendgästehaus „Maxim Gorki"**
**Zum Wilden Graben 12, 99425 Weimar**
**✆ (0 36 43) 85 07 50, Fax 85 07 49**
**JH-Mutter: Danuta Keller**

| | |
|---|---|
| **Träger** | Landesverband Thüringen e.V. |
| **Geöffnet** | 24 Stunden |
| **Geschlossen** | 22.12. bis 27.12. |
| **Raumangebot** | 60 Betten, 1 Tagesraum, vorwiegend familiengerechte Zimmer, 1 Seminarraum, Speiseraum, Kellerbar mit Disco |
| **Lage** | Das JGH liegt unmittelbar am Ortseingang von Weimar, in einer der schönsten Wohngegenden der Stadt. Die Altstadt ist in ca. 10 min. zu Fuß zu erreichen. |
| **Freizeit** | Tischtennis, Grillen, Discothek, im Ort: Frei- und Hallenbad, Reiten, Bowling, Tennis, Theater und Museen der Klassikerstadt |
| **Anreise** | Auto/Bus: A 4 bis Abfahrt Weimar, Parkplatz am Jugendgästehaus Bahn: bis Hbf. Weimar, von hier mit der Stadtlinie 8 bis Haltestelle R.-M.-Rilke-Straße |
| **Eignung** | Freizeiten, Wanderer, Familien, Seminare, Tagungen, Lehrgänge, Gruppen, Einzelgäste |
| **Besonderes** | Die JH ist bedingt für Rollstuhlfahrer geeignet. |

**Nächste Jugendherbergen**
Weimar 1 km, Erfurt 20 km

Name _____ Datum _____

1. What is the local phone number of this youth hostel?

   _____

2. Which area code would you have to dial in Germany if you were to make the
   phone call from outside the city of Weimar?

   _____

3. Besides calling, how else could you contact this youth hostel? Name two
   possibilities.

   _____

4. What person would you contact at this youth hostel *(JH = Jugendherberge)?*

   _____

5. What is the zip code for the city of Weimar?

   _____

6. Can you name the three leisure-time activities that this youth hostel is
   offering on its premises?

   _____

7. How can you get to this youth hostel?

   _____

8. How far is the city of Erfurt from this youth hostel?

   _____

# KAPITEL 2

## Lektion B

**6** **Complete the following dialog using the most appropriate words from the list. You will not need all the words listed.**

| | | | | |
|---|---|---|---|---|
| später | fünf | wie | gegen | echt |
| es | heute | rüber | drei | viel |

*Anne:* Wie viel Uhr ist _____?

*Sarah:* Halb _____.

*Anne:* Hast du _____ Zeit?

*Sarah:* Ja, ich habe _____ Zeit.

*Anne:* Kommst du _____?

*Sarah:* Ja, _____ sechs.

*Anne:* Komm doch schon um _____!

*Sarah:* Na gut. Bis _____!

**7** **Sofie enjoys sketching her relatives. Using complete sentences, tell how old the various people are.**

*Beispiel:*

Onkel Rudi (70)
Onkel Rudi ist siebzig.

1.

Tante Gudrun (65)

_____

2.   Uli (12)

    _____

3.   Katja (17)

    _____

4.   Sabines Vater (43)

    _____

5.   Sabines Großvater (71)

    _____

6.   Onkel Ingo (56)

    _____

Name _____ Datum _____

**8** *Wie viel Uhr ist es?* **Write the answers in complete sentences.**

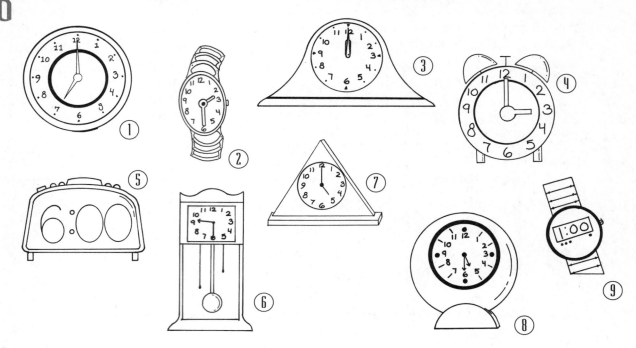

1. _____

2. _____

3. _____

4. _____

5. _____

6. _____

7. _____

8. _____

9. _____

**9** *Internationale Vorwahlen.* **When making international calls from Germany, you enter the international** *Vorwahlnummer* **first before entering any area codes and local numbers. In looking at the various national codes, you'll notice that each starts with "00" followed by different national numbers. Write each national code that follows "00." You should be able to recognize the countries presented in German but listed in English.**

---

*Internationale Vorwahlen*

| | | | |
|---|---|---|---|
| Argentinien | 0054 | Kanada | 001 |
| Australien | 0061 | Liechtenstein | 004175 |
| Belgien | 0032 | Luxemburg | 00352 |
| Brasilien | 0055 | Mexiko | 0052 |
| Dänemark | 0045 | Neuseeland | 0064 |
| Finnland | 00358 | Niederlande | 0031 |
| Frankreich | 0033 | Norwegen | 0047 |
| Griechenland | 0030 | Österreich | 0043 |
| Grönland | 00299 | Polen | 0048 |
| Großbritannien | | Schweden | 0046 |
| und Irland | 0044 | Schweiz | 0041 |
| Island | 00354 | Spanien | 0034 |
| Italien | 0039 | Vereinigte Staaten | |
| Japan | 0081 | von Amerika | 001 |

---

*Beispiel:*  Norway
       *siebenundvierzig*

1. Netherlands

   _____

2. Australia

   _____

3. Mexico

   _____

4. Great Britain

   _____

5. USA

   _____

6. France

   _____

7. Japan

   _____

8. Italy

   _____

**10** Similar to the United States, Germans have access to different long-distance telephone services. Review the chart below and then answer the questions. Write the numbers in German. The chart lists the phone rates per minute. (Note: *Werktage* workdays, *fern ab* distance over; *nah bis* distance within; *Vorwahl* area code, prefix; *Cent* = cent [100 Cent = 1 Euro])

### TELEFONTARIFTABELLE

#### WERKTAGE

| FERN ab 20 km | Vorwahl | Cent | 18 bis 20 Uhr | | Cent | 9 bis 17 Uhr | | Cent |
|---|---|---|---|---|---|---|---|---|
| **6 bis 7 Uhr** | | | Arcor | 01070 | 3 | Teldafax | 01030 | 4 |
| Super 24 | 01024 | 2 | Super 24 | 01024 | 3 | Super24 | 01024 | 4 |
| Interoute | 01066 | 3 | Deutsche Telekom | | 7 | Deutsche Telekom | | 5 |
| Deutsche Telekom | | 4 | **20 bis 21 Uhr** | | | **17 bis 18 Uhr** | | |
| **7 bis 8 Uhr** | | | OneTel | 01086 | 2 | Interoute | 01066 | 4 |
| Super 24 | 01024 | 2 | Arcor | 01070 | 3 | Teldafax | 01030 | 4 |
| Interoute | 01066 | 3 | Deutsche Telekom | | 7 | Deutsche Telekom | | 5 |
| Deutsche Telekom | | 14 | **21 bis 6 Uhr** | | | **18 bis 20 Uhr** | | |
| **8 bis 9 Uhr** | | | OneTel | 01086 | 2 | Teldafax | 01030 | 2 |
| Super 24 | 01024 | 3 | Super24 | 01024 | 2 | Super 24 | 01024 | 3 |
| Viatel | 01079 | 3 | Deutsche Telekom | | 4 | Deutsche Telekom | | 4 |
| Deutsche Telekom | | 14 | NAH bis 20 km | | Cent | **20 bis 21 Uhr** | | |
| **9 bis 17 Uhr** | | | **6 bis 8 Uhr** | | | OneTel | 01086 | 2 |
| Super 24 | 01024 | 4 | Super 24 | 01024 | 2 | Teldafax | 01030 | 2 |
| Interoute | 01066 | 4 | Teldafax | 01030 | 2 | Deutsche Telekom | | 4 |
| Deutsche Telekom | | 14 | Deutsche Telekom | | 4 | **21 bis 6 Uhr** | | |
| **17 bis 18 Uhr** | | | **8 bis 9 Uhr** | | | Super24 | 01024 | 2 |
| Interoute | 01066 | 4 | Teldafax | 01030 | 2 | Teldafax | 01030 | 2 |
| Super 24 | 01024 | 4 | Super24 | 01024 | 3 | Deutsche Telekom | | 3 |
| Deutsche Telekom | | 14 | Deutsche Telekom | | 4 | | | |

*Beispiel:* What is the prefix you have to enter to call *Interoute?*
   null eins null sechs sechs

1. How much is the cheapest call per minute between six and seven in the morning?

   _____

2. How much does the most expensive company charge per minute?

   _____

3. Which area code would you enter if you were to use *Teldafax?*

   _____

4. During which time period are the rates the lowest?

   _____

5. How much does *Deutsche Telecom* charge between 7 A.M. and 8 A.M. when calling beyond 20 kilometers?

   _____

6. How much does *Viatel* charge for one minute?

   _____

7 During which time periods does *Super 24* charge its 2-cent-per-minute rate when calling someone within 20 kilometers?

_____

_____

8. How many *Werktage* are there?

_____

## 11 *der, die* oder *das?*

1. _____ Ecke

2. _____ Minute

3. _____ Herr

4. _____ Tante

5. _____ Mädchen

6. _____ Tag

7. _____ Großmutter

8. _____ Bruder

9. _____ Telefon

10. _____ Freundin

11. _____ Opa

12. _____ Familie

13. _____ Onkel

14. _____ Frau

**12** *Was passt hier?* Answer each question using the appropriate response from the list. Write the response on the line provided.

> Zu Hause.    Ist das nicht die Rockgruppe?    Nicht heute.
>
> Ich höre Musik.    Sonntag.    In Hamburg.    Ja, um wie viel Uhr?
>
> Nein, ich habe vier.    Im Norden.    Es ist neun.

1. Wo ist sie?

   _____

2. Wo ist Cuxhaven?

   _____

3. Was machst du jetzt?

   _____

4. Kennst du Pastell?

   _____

5. Kommst du rüber?

   _____

6. Hast du viel Zeit?

   _____

7. Wo wohnst du?

   _____

8. Was ist heute?

   _____

9. Hast du eine CD?

   _____

10. Wie viel Uhr ist es?

   _____

## 13 Complete the sentences based on the *Lesestück*.

1. Jana wohnt in _____.

2. Das ist eine Stadt im _____.

3. Hat Jana heute viel _____?

4. Kommt Janas _____ vielleicht mit in die Stadt?

5. Carmen _____ Musik.

6. Steffen _____ auch mit in die Stadt.

7. Sie gehen zum _____.

8. Jana und Steffen _____ um vier Uhr in die Stadt.

9. Die Auswahl im Kaufhaus ist _____.

10. Steffen _____ die CD von der Pastell-Rockgruppe.

## 14 Unscramble these letters to spell either days of the week or numbers.

1. ZESEHCHN _____

2. OGMTNA _____

3. AONGSNT _____

4. EVRI _____

5. BSNEEI _____

6. AFITERG _____

7. WGNZZAI _____

8. CMTHOTIW _____

**15** **Complete the following sentences.**

1. Um wie viel Uhr kommt _____?

2. Was machst _____?

3. Robert ist _____.

4. Anke ist Uwes _____.

5. Herr Held hat _____.

6. Sie kommen _____.

7. Die Rockgruppe ist _____.

8. Ich kenne die CD _____.

9. Es ist _____.

10. Die Auswahl ist nicht _____.

**16** **Complete each sentence using an appropriate word.**

1. Manuela ist ein _____.

2. München ist eine _____.

3. Sonja wohnt gleich um die _____.

4. Mittwoch ist ein _____.

5. Maria ist am _____.

6. Rainer hat tolle _____.

7. Stefan ist ein _____.

8. Pastell ist eine _____.

**17** **Fill in the missing letters to form words. The missing letters, when read in sequence, tell you if your answers are correct.**

1. _____ONNERSTAG

2. _____USWAHL

3. _____PÄT

4. _____HR

5. _____OHN

6. _____OLL

7. _____OCKGRUPPE

8. _____N

9. _____D

10. _____ERR

11. _____ELEFON

12. _____ST

13. _____UT

**18** *Am Telefon.* **Imagine that you and your classmates are traveling through Switzerland. You are staying in Lucerne *(Luzern)* for a week. During that time several of your classmates encounter problems, and your teacher selects you as class representative to get some assistance. For each situation, write the name of the place or organization you contact, as well as the phone number (include numerical digits and written numbers. One of your classmates...**

# REISEINFORMATION
## *Travel Information*
## Luzern *Lucerne*

**CAMPING LIDO** *Camping Lido*

Im Bahnhof / *Train Station*
31 21 46

**FUNDBÜRO** *Lost & Found*

Burgerstrasse
21 78 08

**RAIL-SERVICE**

Bahnhof / *Train Station* (Fr. 1,40/Min.)
157 33 33

**TOURIST INFORMATION**

Frankenstrasse
51 71 71

**WETTER INFORMATION** *Weather Information*

162

**FLUGGEPÄCK-SERVICE** *Flight Luggage Service*

Bahnhof, Schalter 21 7.00–19.00
21 32 61
*Train Station, Window 21
7.00 A.M. – 7 P.M.*

Ohne amerikanische und einigen weiteren Fluggesellschaften frühestens 24 Std. vor Abflug, spätestens 5 Std. vor Abflug ab Zürich-Flughafen oder Vortag bis 19.00.

*Does not include American airline companies and several other airlines. Earliest check-in 24 hours before departure from Zurich airport or day before until 7 P.M.*

**FEUERWEHR-NOTRUF** *Fire Dept. Emergency*

118

**FLUGBESTÄTIGUNG** *Flight Confirmation*

Bitte kontaktieren Sie Ihre Fluggesellschaft in Zürich City oder Zürich Flughafen,
01 258 34 34.

*Please contact your airline in Zurich or Zurich airport, 01 258 34 34.*

**POLIZEINOTRUF** *Police Emergency*

117

**SANITÄTSNOTRUF** *Ambulance*

144

*Beispiel:* wanted to have the flight reconfirmed.
FLUGBESTÄTIGUNG (01 258 34 34 / null eins - zweihundertachtundfünfzig - vierunddreißig - vierunddreißig)

1. ...lost his or her passport.

_____

_____

2.  ...witnessed a fire and wants to notify the appropriate organization.

_____

_____

3.  ...wants to know when the train leaves for Frankfurt.

_____

_____

4.  ...saw an accident and wants to call an ambulance.

_____

_____

5.  ...wants to check into camping facilities at Campground Lido.

_____

_____

6.  ...wants to inquire about the cost of storing a suitcase at the train station for a week.

_____

_____

7.  ...witnessed a theft and wants to call the police.

_____

_____

8.  ...wants to get some information about Lucerne and surroundings.

_____

_____

9.  ...wants to find out about flight arrivals and departures.

_____

_____

10.  ...wants to know about weather conditions in the Swiss Alps.

_____

_____

# 19 *Kreuzworträtsel*

## WAAGERECHT

1. ___ gehen Steffen und Jana?
4. Was ___ du heute?
7. Carmen hört ___.
8. Hast du heute viel ___?
10. Jana ___ am Telefon.
12. Die CD ist ganz ___.
13. Zwanzig minus sechzehn ist ___.
14. Julia ist ___.

## SENKRECHT

2. Julia ist zu ___.
3. ___ du um fünf Uhr rüber?
5. Alexanders ___ heißt Julia.
6. Jana und Steffen gehen zum Kaufhaus in die ___.
7. Heute ist Mittwoch. ___ ist Donnerstag.
9. ___ ist schon spät.
11. Die Rockgruppe ist ___.
13. Wie ___ Uhr ist es?

Name _____ Datum _____

# KAPITEL 3

## Lektion A

**1** **Look at each illustration and describe in one sentence what the various people are doing.**

*Beispiel:*

Paul
Paul spielt Klavier.

1.

Gisela und Anke

_____

2.

Tanja

_____

3.

Julia und Robert

_____

4.

Timo

_____

5.

Wolf und Peter

_____

6.   Susanne und Udo

_____

7.   der Junge und das Mädchen

_____

8.   Herr und Frau Krüger

_____

## 2  Complete the sentences using the words listed.

| Buch | Basketball | Uhr | Auswahl | Blechtrommel | Videothek |
|------|------------|-----|---------|--------------|-----------|
| Computerspiele | | | Disko | Deutsch | Film |

1. In _____ lesen sie ein Buch von Grass.

2. Der _____ dauert bis halb acht Uhr.

3. Um wie viel _____ kommst du rüber? Um vier Uhr.

4. Sarah und Tobias gehen zur _____.

5. Das _____ von Günter Grass ist sehr bekannt.

6. Spielst du _____? Ja, sehr gern.

7. Wir gehen in die _____ und tanzen dort.

8. Was hast du da? Zwei _____ für meinen Computer.

9. Die _____ an Videos ist im Kaufhaus sehr groß.

10. „Die _____" ist ein interessantes Buch.

**3** **Complete each sentence based on the illustrations.**

*Beispiel:*

Peter spielt gern ___.
Gitarre

1.

Wir _____ gern _____.

2.

Möchtest du _____ spielen?

3.

Morgen _____ Herr und Frau Siebert.

4.

Spielt ihr später _____?

5.

Wer spielt _____?

6.

Ich _____ gern einen Krimi.

Name _____ Datum _____

 **Complete the following dialog using the words listed.**

| | | | | |
|---|---|---|---|---|
| machst | *interessant* | spät | gern | nicht |
| möchtest | gegen | zu | lese | mit | gehe | bekannt |

*Sven:* Was _____ du gern?

*Hans:* Ich spiele _____ Fußball.

*Sven:* Ich _____ .

*Hans:* So? Was _____ du denn machen?

*Sven:* Ich _____ gern einen Krimi.

*Hans:* Das ist doch nicht so _____ .

*Sven:* Oh ja, mein Krimi ist ganz interessant und er ist auch sehr

_____ .

*Hans:* Ich _____ jetzt zu Angelika.

*Sven:* Na, dann komme ich auch _____ .

*Hans:* Komm doch so _____ sieben Uhr.

*Sven:* So _____ ?

*Hans:* Ja, dann ist sie _____ Hause.

**Write the appropriate forms of *haben*.**

1. _____ du einen Bruder oder eine Schwester?

2. Um halb neun _____ wir keine Zeit.

3. _____ ihr einen Fußball?

4. Wir _____ vier Karten für das Rockkonzert.

5. Ich _____ ein Video.

6. _____ Gisela einen Freund?

7. Herr und Frau Schmidt _____ jetzt einen Computer.

8. Lisa _____ einen tollen Krimi.

**6** *Was weißt du?* **Many young Germans follow the various national, regional and local soccer games every week. Look at the newspaper report of regional and local games and answer the questions that follow.**

---

## FUSSBALL

### Regionalliga Süd

**VfB Stuttgart Amat. - SV Lohhof 3:0 (1:0):** Zuschauer: 250. – Tore: 1:0 Haas (42.), 2:0 Haas (73.), 3:0 Haas (90.). – Gelb-rote Karte: Himsel (Lohhof/66.).
**SSV Reutlingen - TSF Ditzingen 6:0 (4:0):** Zuschauer 3050. – Tore: 1:0 Becker (4.), 2:0 Cast (8.), 3:0 Hoffmann (12.), 4:0 Djappa (36.), 5:0 Hofacker (62., Foulelfmeter), 6:0 Lapaczinski.
**FSV Frankfurt - SV Wehen 0:0:** Zuschauer: 1500. – Rote Karte: Pereira (Frankfurt/89.).
**SC Pfullendorf - FC 05 Schweinfurt 3:1 (1:0):** Zuschauer: 1550. – Tore: 1:0 Magdic (28.), 1:1 Roegele (51.), 2:1 Barlecaj (53., Foulelfmeter), 3:1 Simon (77.).
**FC Bayern München/Amat. - VfR Mannheim 2:2 (1:2):** Zuschauer: 600. – Tore: 0:1 Ziegler (10.), 1:1 Jarolim (14., Foulelfmeter), 1:2 Petry (43.), 2:2 Banaczek (79.).
**SV Darmstadt - Borussia Fulda 3:1 (1:0):** Zuschauer: 3500. – Tore: 1:0 Wölki (19.), 2:0 Wölki (48.), 3:0 Dzemaili (61.), 3:1 Nadaroglu (90., Eigentor).
**Karlsruher SC Amat. - TSV 1860 München Amat. 0:2 (0:0):** Zuschauer: 600. – Tore: 0:1 Fröhlich (52.), 0:2 Bernhardt (90.).

### Bayernliga

**TSV Aindling - FC Bayern Hof 0:0:** Zuschauer: 900.

**SpVgg Stegaurach - SpVgg Ansbach 2:2 (1:0):** Zuschauer: 650. – Tore: 1:0 Hartmann (26.), 2:0 Büttner (63.), 2:1 Fröhlich (73.), 2:2 Fröhlich (94.).
**1. FC Nürnberg Amat. - SpVgg Landshut 3:3 (2:0):** Zuschauer: 124. – Tore: 1:0 Müller (4.), 2:0 Frei (35.), 3:0 Christ (56.), 3:1 Cofarriello (57.), 3:2 Radlmeier (70., Handelfmeter), 3:3 Kammermeier (86.).
**FC Starnberg - Würzburger FV 5:0 (2:0):** Zuschauer: 250. – Tore: 1:0 Suchanke (16.), 2:0 Staude (29.), 3:0 Suchanke (60.), 4:0 Tekes (79.), 5:0 Palic (90.). – Gelb-Rote Karten: Grönert (Würzburg/56.).
**Schwaben Augsburg - 1. FC Feucht 2:1 (1:0):** Zuschauer: 300. – Tore: 1:0 Scheurer (32.), 2:0 Abazi (53.) 2:1 Krakowczyk (66.).
**SC 04 Schwabach - SpVgg Weiden 0:0:** Zuschauer: 350. – Gelb-rote Karte: Vogel (Weiden/83.).
**1. FC Passau - Jahn Regensburg 1:4 (0:3):** Zuschauer: 700. – Tore: 0:1 Holm (4.), 0:2 Mayer (12.), 0:3 Brand (19.), 1:3 Mojzis (56.), 1:4 Brand (91.). – Gelbrote Karten: Zschiedrich (Passau/86.).
**FC Kempten - FC Memmingen 2:1 (1:1):** Zuschauer: 1500. – Tore: 1:0 Hörburger (9.), 1:1 Hebel (44.), 2:1 Ferreiro (87.). – Gelb-rote Karten: Lindinger (Memmingen/89.).
**SC Weismain - Jahn Forchheim 2:3 (2:1):** Zuschauer: 400. – Tore: 1:0 Klaus (11.), 1:2 Aksoy (14.), 2:1 Nußlein (16.), 2:2 Bintig (58.), 2:3 Seitz (68.).

---

1. How many spectators watched the game between Darmstadt and Fulda?

   _____

2. Who scored a goal in the 19th minute in the game between 1. FC Passau and Jahn Regensburg?

   _____

3. Who was FC Memmingen's opponent?

   _____

4. What was the final score between SSV Reutlingen and TSF Ditzingen?

   _____

5. How many goals were scored in the game between FSV Frankfurt and SV Wehen?

   _____

6. How many goals did Suchanke score for his FC Starnberg team?

_____

7. When was the last goal scored in the game between SC Pfullendorf and FC 05 Schweinfurt?

_____

8. Which game had the fewest number of spectators? How many?

_____

**7** **Rewrite the following sentences by beginning each with the time element. Watch the word order.**

*Beispiel:* Werner spielt heute Tennis.
Heute spielt Werner Tennis.

1. Wir gehen jetzt in die Stadt.

_____

2. Heike und Uwe möchten um acht Uhr zum Rockkonzert gehen.

_____

3. Ich höre um halb sieben gern Musik.

_____

4. Sie spielen um vier Uhr Fußball.

_____

5. Hans geht um zwei Uhr schwimmen.

_____

6. Frau Teubner kommt morgen rüber.

_____

7. Der Film beginnt um acht Uhr.

_____

8. Wir spielen heute Basketball.

_____

# KAPITEL 3

## Lektion B

**8  Write two possible answers to the question *Wie viel Uhr ist es?***

*Beispiel:*

Es ist zehn Minuten nach zwei.
Es ist vierzehn Uhr zehn.
Es ist zwei Uhr zehn.

1.

_____

_____

2.

_____

_____

3.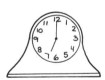

_____

_____

4.

_____

_____

5. 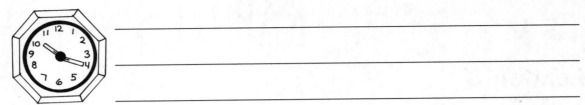 _____

_____

_____

6. 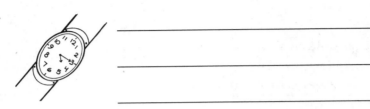 _____

_____

_____

7. 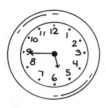 _____

_____

_____

8. _____

_____

_____

**9** ***Um wie viel Uhr beginnt das Fernsehprogramm...?*** **Besides *ARD* and *ZDF*, there are other major TV stations such as *Bayerisches Fernsehen, RTL* and *SAT 1* that enjoy a strong following among German TV viewers. Tell when each program begins and on which station. Note that *Bayerisches Fernsehen* changes to *im Bayerischen Fernsehen* as in the example. Also, the beginning quotation in German is usually placed at the bottom of the line, before the first letter.**

| **Bayerisches Fernsehen** | **RTL** | **SAT.1** |
|---|---|---|
| **6.00** Panoramabilder **8.45** Tele-Gym **9.00** Fliege **10.00** Schuhbecks **10.30** Reportage am Sonntag. Adlerauge sei wachsam! Artenschützer im Einsatz für Greifvögel. **11.00** Aus Schwaben und Altbayern **11.40** Sport-Tribüne **12.00** Frankenschau **12.40** Sport regional **13.00** Telekolleg: Deutsch **13.30** Die Straße der Wildnis **14.15** Clin d'oeil. Magazin in französischer Sprache **14.30** Stoffe und Stoffkreisläufe. Baustoffe. Film von Anita Bach **15.00** Schlawiner Platz. Floris Zapp Zarapp. Kindermagazin **15.30** Pinocchio. Der Wunderdoktor. Japan. Zeichentrick-Serie **16.00** Kochen mit Kindern **16.10** Curiosity Show **16.20** Kochen mit Kindern. Quark, Joghurt, Milch und Käse **16.30** Schau mal! **16.35** Wie Hund und Katze. Großmutter streikt. | **6.00** Punkt 6. Magazin mit Wolfram Kons **6.30** Guten Morgen Deutschland. Magazin **7.00** Punkt 7. Magazin **7.35** Reich und schön (2304). US-Familien-Serie **7.55** Unter uns. Familien-Serie (Wh.) ⊙ **8.25** Gute Zeiten, schlechte Zeiten. Familien-Serie (Wh.) ⊙ **9.00** Mein Morgen. Magazin mit Anne Gesthuysen und Tanja Paidar **10.30** Sabrina. Talk-Show. Thema: Ich mache Party bis zum Umfallen ⊙ **11.30** familien duell. Spiel mit Werner Schulze-Erdel **12.00** Punkt 12. Mittagsjournal mit Katja Burkard **13.00** Die Oliver Geissen Show. Talk-Show ⊙ **14.00** Birte Karalus. Talk-Show ⊙ **15.00** Bärbel Schäfer. Talk-Show. Thema: Du bist viel zu schade für diesem Typen ⊙ **16.00** Hans Meiser. Talk-Show. Thema: Wirst du dich heute ändern? ⊙ | **5.30** Frühstücksfernsehen **9.00** Mission: Impossible – In geheimer Mission. Der Camagua-Putsch. US-Agenten-Serie **10.00** Geliebte Schwestern. Krankenhaus-Serie ⊙ **10.30** Geliebte Schwestern. Krankenhaus-Serie (VPS 10.29) **11.00** Jörg Pilawa. Talk-Show. Thema: Vaters Neue ist ein Albtraum **12.00** Vera am Mittag. Talk-Show. Thema: Du bist eine Rabenmutter! **13.00** Sonja. Talk-Show. Thema: Selbst Schuld! Du hast mich in die Arme eines anderen getrieben **14.00** Ricky! Talk-Show. Thema: Versteh's endlich: Das war nur ein One Night Stand; anschl. Nachrichten **15.00** Star Trek: Deep Space Nine. Die Front. US-Science-Fiction-Serie ⊙; anschl. Nachrichten **16.00** Chicago Hope – Endstation Hoffnung. Des Rätsels Lösung. US-Krankenhaus-Serie |
| **17.00** Rundschau **17.02** Lateinamerika – Der entwurzelte Kontinent (5). Ruinen, Rituale und Romane. Reihe von Gernot Schley **17.45** Bayern live – Abendschau. Mit Sport | **17.00** Die Nanny. Der blinde Passagier. US-Comedy-Serie ⊙ **17.30** Unter uns (1196). Familien-Serie ⊙ | **17.00** Jeder gegen Jeden. Quizshow mit Hans-Hermann Gockel **17.30** 17:30 – Live aus Berlin. Deutschlandmagazin (oder Regionalprogramme) |
| **18.00** Rundschau **18.05** Bayern live – Abendschau **18.30** Bayern live – Regionalprogramme **18.43** Programmvorschau **18.45** Rundschau | **18.00** Guten Abend RTL. Ländermagazin mit Laura Lange (oder Regionalprogramme) **18.30** Exclusiv – Das Star-Magazin. Mit Frauke Ludowig **18.45** RTL aktuell | **18.00** Richterin Barbara Salesch. Echte Fälle, echte Urteile. Gerichtsshow **18.30** 18:30. Nachrichten **18.47** Wetter **18.50** täglich ran – Sport |

*Beispiele: Schuhbecks*

Das Fernsehprogramm „Schuhbecks" beginnt um zehn Uhr am Morgen im Bayerischen Fernsehen.

*Star Trek*

Das Fernsehprogramm „Star Trek" beginnt um drei Uhr am Nachmittag im SAT 1.

1. *Das Star-Magazin*

_____

_____

2. *täglich ran – Sport*

_____

_____

3. *Panoramabilder*

_____

_____

4. *Pinocchio*

_____

_____

5. *Das Wetter*

_____

_____

6. *Frankenschau*

_____

_____

7. *Frühstücksfernsehen*

_____

_____

8. *Die Bärbel Schäfer Talk Show*

_____

_____

## 10 Match the questions on the left with the most appropriate answers on the right

_____ 1. Wohin gehst du so schnell?

_____ 2. Was gibt's jetzt im Fernsehen?

_____ 3. Wie spät ist es denn?

_____ 4. Was spielst du später?

_____ 5. Wann machst du deine Hausaufgaben?

_____ 6. Was ist ganz neu?

_____ 7. Seht ihr später fern?

_____ 8. Ist es schon acht Uhr?

_____ 9. Wo ist Karsten denn?

_____10. Was macht ihr hier in der Videothek?

A. Ja. Der Film ist wirklich toll.

B. Wir holen ein Video.

C. Heute Nachmittag.

D. Nein, viel später.

E. Nach Hause.

F. Vielleicht Fußball.

G. Die Sportschau.

H. Mein Computer.

I. Viertel vor zwölf.

J. Zu Hause.

## 11 Form three sentences each, using the phrases *zu Hause* and *nach Hause*.

1. _____

2. _____

3. _____

4. _____

5. _____

6. _____

**12** Complete the narrative using the correct forms of the verbs listed. The information is based on the *Lesestück*.

| | | | | | |
|---|---|---|---|---|---|
| machen | kennen | sagen | wohnen | spielen | sehen |
| haben | bleiben | kommen | sein | | |

Sonja _____ in Wilhelmshaven. Das _____ eine

Stadt im Norden. Sie und ihre Freundin Claudia _____ aus dem

Kaufhaus und _____ auch gleich Heiko und Marco. Beide

Mädchen _____ die zwei Jungen gut.

Am Sonntag _____ eine bekannte Band in Wilhelmshaven.

Claudia _____ eine Karte für das Konzert. Tilo

_____ zwei Wochen bei Marco. Sonja _____:

„Ich habe eine Idee." Sie _____ mit Claudias Schwester die

Hausaufgaben.

**13** Form phrases by adding appropppriate verbs.

*Beispiel:* zu Hause ___
zu Hause sein

1. Musik _____

2. viel Zeit _____

3. ein Video _____

4. zum Kaufhaus _____

5. bei den Hausaufgaben _____

6. Tennis _____

7. ein Buch _____

8. aus Hamburg _____

9. ein Fernsehprogramm _____

10. Hamburg gut _____

**14** **Complete the following conversations by writing complete sentences.**

Was machst du später?

_____

Was gibt's denn im Fernsehen?

_____

Ich möchte den Krimi auch sehen.

_____

Ich komme dann zehn Minuten vor acht.

_____

***

Kennst du Martina?

_____

Sie ist neu hier.

_____

Aus Ulm.

_____

Im Süden.

_____

Sie hat eine Schwester.

**15** Fill in the missing words, writing each in capital letters. The first letters, when read in sequence, refer to a person who is smart.

1. Klaus geht um halb acht Uhr am Morgen in die _____.

2. Warum hast du Computerspiele? Ich habe doch einen _____ zu Hause.

3. Hast du heute viele _____? Nein, nur etwas für Deutsch.

4. Was _____ ihr? Ein Buch.

5. Um wie viel Uhr beginnen die Nachrichten? Um sechs Uhr am _____.

6. Am Sonnabend _____ am Sonntag spielt eine Band in Wilhelmshaven.

7. Heiko und Marco gehen zum _____. Heikos Cousin kommt aus Dresden.

8. Hast du _____ Zeit? Oh ja, ich habe viel Zeit.

9. Für das _____ gibt es keine Karten mehr.

10. Wie _____ dir dieser Film? Er ist wirklich toll.

11. Sonja kennt Tilo. _____ ist immer im Sommer da.

12. Kommst du _____? Ja, aber nicht vor sieben Uhr.

**16** Write complete statements or questions using the words in the same sequence as shown. You will need to add words to complete some sentences.

*Beispiel:* Sonnabend / haben / ich / viel Zeit
Am Sonnabend habe ich viel Zeit.

1. Wann / beginnen / Fernsehprogramm

_____

2. Kennen / du / meinen Freund / aus Deutschland

_____

3. Was / machen / du / Sonntag

_____

4. Ich / haben / Computer

_____

5. Gehen / ihr / sechs Uhr / Bahnhof

_____

6. Susi / spielen / Nachmittag / Computerspiele

_____

7. Buch / sein / sehr interessant

_____

8. hören / ihr / später / Rockmusik

_____

**17** **Form questions by asking for the italicized words.**

*Beispiel:* Wir gehen *morgen* zu Tante Anita.
Wann gehen wir zu Tante Anita?

1. *Katrin* möchte zum Rockkonzert.

_____

2. Bernds Großmutter wohnt *in Berlin.*

_____

3. Heute Nachmittag gehen sie *zum Kaufhaus.*

_____

4. Frau Rüdiger kommt *aus Bremen.*

_____

5. Angelika und Gabi spielen *Tennis.*

_____

6. Dresden ist *eine Stadt.*

_____

7. *Ulis Vater* ist jetzt in Deutschland.

_____

8. Wir holen *vier Karten.*

_____

## 18  Beantworte diese Fragen!

1. Was machst du am Sonntag?

   _____

2. Was spielst du gern?

   _____

3. Warum hast du keine Zeit?

   _____

4. Was gibt's heute Abend im Fernsehen?

   _____

5. Welche Rockgruppe hast du gern?

   _____

## 19 *Kreuzworträtsel*

### WAAGERECHT

2. Wie gefällt ___ diese Musik?

4. ___ du Karten für das Konzert?

5. Wie viele Stunden ___ es, bis ihr kommt?

6. Für diesen Film gibt es ___ Karten mehr.

9. Wohin gehst du? Zum ___.

10. Wo bleibt denn Dieter? ___ ist noch zu Hause.

11. Wohin gehst du? Nach ___.

12. Günter Grass ist sehr ___.

13. Ich ___ gern Basketball.

14. In der ___ sehen wir am Sonntag Nachmittag Fußball und Tennis.

### SENKRECHT

1. Um sieben Uhr kommen die ___ im Fernsehen.

2. Wohin gehen wir heute? In die ___.

3. Holt ihr ein ___ in der Videothek?

4. In Englisch habe ich heute viele ___.

7. ___ kommst du nicht mit? Ich habe keine Zeit.

8. Was macht ihr? Wir sehen ___.

9. Um wie viel Uhr ___ der Film?

13. Tilo ist ___ nett und charmant.

# KAPITEL 4

## Lektion A

**1** *Was ist das?* **Identify each object including its article.** *Auf Deutsch, bitte!*

1. _____

2. _____

3. _____

4. _____

5. _____

6. _____

7. _____

8. _____

9. _____

10. _____

Name _____ Datum _____

## 2 Look at the illustration and write what these students might be talking about.

_____

_____

_____

_____

_____

_____

_____

_____

_____

_____

_____

Name _____ Datum _____

**3** Ten classroom objects are hidden in the word find below. The letters may go backward or forward; they may go up, down, across or diagonally. However, they go only one way in any one word. Can you find all of them?

E D I E R K G S U B

H I D H C U B A H N

C S A L M L R E R K

S A U M W I V P Q O

A S I F R Z A X N P

T A F E L P D G M E

L B L E I S T I F T

U Q K E N D G U F F

H U R J E R T S N E

C D H U A Z H I G H

S H O V L R I K W D

## 4  Fill in the appropriate form of the definite article using *der, die, das,* or *den.*

1. Kennst du _____ Mädchen?

2. Hörst du _____ Musik?

3. _____ Telefon ist hier.

4. _____ Lehrer kommt heute später.

5. Bringst du _____ Computerspiel mit?

6. Wo ist _____ Kuli?

7. Hast du _____ Papier?

8. Wir kaufen _____ Computer.

9. _____ Krimi ist ganz interessant.

10. Ist _____ Uhr nicht da?

11. Holen Sie _____ Bleistift?

12. Sabine kauft _____ Buch.

## 5  Write complete statements or questions using the words in the same sequence as shown. You will need to add appropriate words and endings.

1. Wo / kaufen / du / Landkarte

   _____

2. Herr / kommen / neun Uhr

   _____

3. Wir / kennen / Computerspiel

   _____

4. Kaufen / ihr / Gitarre

   _____

5. Ich / brauchen / Rechner

   _____

6. Computer / sein / ganz neu

   _____

7. Wann / beginnen / Film

   _____

8. Haben / Anna / Schultasche

   _____

**6** *Schulen.* **The list below represents several schools in the Main-Kinzig area. Write the answers to the questions. The following words might be useful to know:** *Ort* **town,** *Schulart* **type of school;** *Schulleitung* **school administration.**

## Schulen im Main-Kinzig-Kreis

| Ort | Schulart | Straße | Schulleitung | Tel.-Nr. |
|---|---|---|---|---|
| **63571 Gelnhausen** | | | | |
| St. T.Gelnhausen | Philipp-Reis-Schule Grund- u. Hauptschule | Philipp-Reis-Str. 16 | Herr Funk | 06051/2102 15593 |
| St.T. Gelnhausen | Realschule | Jahnstraße | Herr Eisenbarth | 06051/17600 17957 |
| St. T. Gelnhausen | Grimmelshausenschule Gymnasium | In der Aue 3 | Herr Kauck | 06051/17008 17009 |
| St. T. Gelnhausen | Berufliche Schulen | Graslitzer-Str. 2-8 | Herr Benzing | 06051/48130 |
| St. T. Hailer | Ysenburgschule Grund- u. Hauptschule | Konr.-Schneid.-Weg 7 | Herr Brand | 06051/69500 |
| St.T. Höchst | Igelsgrundschule Grundschule | Schulstraße | Herr Prinz | 06051/73800 |
| St. T. Roth | Herzbergschule Grundschule | Rathausstraße 1 | Herr Noack | 06051/4031 |
| **63584 Gründau** | | | | |
| OT Hain-Gründau | Grundschule Kinzigtalschule | Klammbornstraße | Herr Neugebauer | 06058/8773 |
| OT Lieblos | Grundschule m. Förderstufe | Büdinger Str. 11 a | Frau Dr. Trinkmann | 06051/5802 |
| OT Mittelgründau | Grundschule | Hofweg 1 | Frau Schickling | 06058/8457 |
| OT Rothenbergen | Anton-Calaminus-Schule Grund,- Haupt- u. Realschule | Niedergründauer .17 | Frau Dreßbach | 06051/2811 |
| **63594 Hasselroth** | | | | |
| OT Gondsroth | Alte Dorfschule Gondsroth Grundschule | Schulstraße | Frau Wudy | 06055/84635 |
| OT Neuenhaßlau | Hasselbachschule, Grundschule | Bornwiesenweg 20 | Frau Bauscher | 06055/2866 |
| OT Niedermittlau | Auwiesenschule, Grundschule | Taunustraße | Frau Iffland | 06055/2611 |
| **63637 Joßgrund** | | | | |
| OT Oberndorf | Grund- u. Hauptschule | Schulstraße | NN | 06059/411 |
| **63589 Linsengericht** | | | | |
| OT Altenhaßlau | Hasela-Schule, Grundschule | Bergstraße | Herr Desch | 06051/71630 |
| OT Altenhaßlau | Brentano-Schule Schule für Lernhilfe | Brentanostr. 1-3 | Frau Jordan | 06051/72066 |
| OT Eidengesäß | Geisbergschule Grund- und Hauptschule mit Förderstufe | Schulstraße | Herr Brand | 06051/71364 |
| OT Altenhaßlau | Martinsschule Schule f. prakt. Bildbare | Brentanostr. 9 | Frau Matzner | 06051/97530 |

1. On what street is the *Geisbergschule* located?

   _____

2. Who is in charge of the administration at the *Herzbergschule?*

   _____

3. What two local phone numbers are listed for the *Gymnasium* located in the town of Gelnhausen?

   _____

4. At which school is Mrs. Matzner the contact person in the administration office?

   _____

5. How many administrators have a Ph.D. (doctor's degree)?

   _____

6. How many elementary schools (can also include those combined with other schools) are there in Linsengericht?

   _____

7. Which school is located at *Jahnstraße?*

   _____

8. What are the area codes for Gründau?

   _____

9. At which three schools is Mrs. Dreßbach employed?

   _____

10. What is the zip code for the town of Joßgrund?

   _____

**7** **Explain the following school-related words. How are they similar or different from your school?**

1. Große Pause:

   _____

   _____

2. Gymnasium:

   _____

   _____

3. Austauschprogramm:

   _____

   _____

4. Mittagspause:

   _____

   _____

5. Klassenausflug:

   _____

   _____

# KAPITEL 4

## Lektion B

**8** *Ein Stundenplan.* **Complete the schedule below, listing the subjects that you are taking and the day and hour during which you take them.**

### Stundenplan

Schule: _____ Klasse: _____

| Zeit | Montag | Dienstag | Mittwoch | Donnerstag | Freitag |
|------|--------|----------|----------|------------|---------|
|      |        |          |          |            |         |
|      |        |          |          |            |         |
|      |        |          |          |            |         |
|      |        |          |          |            |         |
|      |        |          |          |            |         |
|      |        |          |          |            |         |
|      |        |          |          |            |         |
|      |        |          |          |            |         |
|      |        |          |          |            |         |
|      |        |          |          |            |         |
|      |        |          |          |            |         |
|      |        |          |          |            |         |

**9** *Was passt zusammen?* **Find the most appropriate ending for each question.**

_____ 1. Was für ein Fach...      A. der Computer so langsam?

_____ 2. Was ist...               B. schwer?

_____ 3. Wann hast du...          C. dein Lieblingsfach?

_____ 4. Klingelt es...           D. hast du?

_____ 5. Machst du jetzt...       E. deine Hausaufgaben?

_____ 6. Warum ist...             F. schon?

_____ 7. Hat er...                G. wirklich Recht?

_____ 8. Ist die Informatikaufgabe...   H. Englisch?

**10** **Wer? Wen? Was?** Choose one of these questions words to complete each sentence.

1. _____ ist zu Hause?

2. _____ kennst du? Gabi und Susi.

3. _____ sagst du?

4. _____ kommt zu spät?

5. _____ wohnt in Köln?

6. _____ spielt ihr gern?

7. _____ bringt sie mit, Uwe oder Kai?

8. _____ machst du heute Nachmittag?

**11** **Beantworte diese Fragen!**

1. Was machst du heute Nachmittag?

   _____

2. Wer ist dein Freund oder deine Freundin?

   _____

3. Wen kennst du in deiner Klasse?

   _____

4. Wer hat viel Zeit?

   _____

5. Was hast du in der Schultasche?

   _____

6. Was gibt's um acht Uhr im Fernsehen?

   _____

**12** **Complete the following narrative based on the *Lesestück*.**

Vanessa ist Manuelas _____. Beide Mädchen wohnen in

Ingolstadt, einer Stadt im Bundesland _____. In der Woche

_____ Manuela vor der Schule zu Vanessa. Bei Vanessa bekommt

sie immer ein _____.

Vanessa ist heute _____. Sie _____ in der ersten

Stunde ihr Lieblingsfach, Erdkunde. In diesem Fach bekommt sie immer eine

_____. Manuela _____ Biologie langweilig.

Vanessa und Manuela _____ schnell. Der _____

kommt in zehn Minuten.

Im Herbst ist es um diese Zeit noch _____. Beide Mädchen

_____ nicht lange. Dann ist der Bus schon da. Mit dem Bus

dauert es nur fünfzehn _____ zur Schule. Vor der ersten Stunde

_____ sie Schulfreunde.

Die erste _____ beginnt zehn Minuten vor acht Uhr. Heute am

Donnerstag haben Manuela und Vanessa _____ Klassen. Um

1.15 _____ gehen sie nach Hause. Sie machen dann die

_____. Manchmal sind beide bei Vanessa und

_____ fern.

**13** Can you identify the following German nouns or names? The first letters, when read in sequence, tell you that your answers are correct.

1. Du bist jetzt in dieser Klasse. In diesem Fach lernst du _____.

2. Diana sagt: „Ich mache noch meine _____.“

3. Bayern liegt in _____.

4. Manuela und Vanessa gehen schon früh in die _____

5. Die Schultasche liegt auf dem _____.

6. Gabrieles Computer ist für die _____ gut genug.

7. _____ ist Vanessas Freundin.

8. Matthias meint: „Die Probleme in _____ sind ganz schwer.“

9. Auf der _____ lesen sie, welche Hausaufgaben sie für morgen haben.

**14** Supply the proper forms of *sein*.

1. Vanessa und Manuela _____ vor acht Uhr in der Schule.

2. _____ ihr heute Abend zu Hause?

3. Wo _____ der Bahnhof?

4. Um wie viel Uhr _____ Herr und Frau Hofer in der Stadt?

5. Warum _____ du denn nicht froh?

6. Jens und Uli _____ da drüben.

7. Ich _____ bis halb zwei Uhr in der Schule.

8. _____ Katharina wirklich so klug?

**15** **Ein Zeugnis.** Lisa Bachmeier is a student at the *Hohenzollern-Gymnasium Sigmaringen.* The grade report below summarizes Lisa's achievements and various other details. Answer each question in the language in which they are asked. (Note: *Verhalten* conduct; *Mitarbeit* participation)

---

**Baden-Württemberg**

**Hohenzollern - Gymnasium Sigmaringen**
**Zeugnis des Gymnasiums**

Klasse     *10a*                                          Schuljahr *2002/2003*

Vor- und Zuname     *Lisa  B a c h m e i e r*

Verhalten:          *gut*               Mitarbeit:     *sehr gut*

Leistungen in den einzelnen Fächern

| | | | |
|---|---|---|---|
| Religionslehre (ev) | *gut* | Mathematik | *gut* |
| | | Physik | *sehr gut* |
| Deutsch | *befriedigend* | Chemie | *befriedigend* |
| Erdkunde | ----- | Biologie | *gut* |
| Geschichte | *gut* | Sport | *gut* |
| Gemeinschaftskunde | *gut* | Musik | *befriedigend* |
| Englisch | *befriedigend* | Bildende Kunst | *gut* |
| Französisch | ----- | Ethik | ----- |
| Latein | *befriedigend* | | |
| Griechisch | ----- | Arbeitsgemeinschaften: | |
| | | Orchester | *teilgenommen* |

Bemerkungen:     wird versetzt und erhält eine Belobung

Datum: 21. Juli 2003

_____               (Dienstsiegel          _____
Schulleiter/in                                    der Schule)          Klassenlehrer/in

Gesehen ! Erziehungsberechtigte/r     _____

**Notenstufen:**   Verhalten und Mitarbeit:  sehr gut (1) = sgt; gut (2) = gut; befriedigend (3) = bfr;unbefriedigend (4) = unbfr;
Leistungen in den Fächern: sehr gut (1) = sgt; gut (2) = gut; befriedigend (3) = bfr;
ausreichend (4) = ausr;  mangelhaft (5) = mgh; ungenügend (6) = ung;

---

1. *Wie viele Fächer hat Lisa?*

_____

2. *Was für eine Note bekommt sie in Mathematik?*

_____

3. *In welchen Fächern bekommt sie eine Drei?*

_____

4. *Ist sie in Biologie schlecht?*

_____

5. *Hat Lisa Französisch?*

_____

6. *In welchem Bundesland liegt Sigmaringen?*

_____

7. How is Lisa's conduct compared to other students? Where does that grade report indicate that?

_____

8. What grade is Lisa in?

_____

9. In which activity (not listed as a school subject) does Lisa participate?

_____

10. Did the teacher make any particular comments about Lisa?

_____

**16** *Ferien in deutschen Schulen.* The following represents a typical school vacation schedule in Germany. Answer this question for each vacation period: *Wie viele Tage haben die Schüler Ferien?*

| Schuljahr | |
| --- | --- |
| Herbst | 14.10. - 19.10. |
| Weihnachten | 20.12. - 04.01. |
| Winter | 10.02. - 15.02. |
| Ostern | 24.03. - 05.04. |
| Pfingsten | 16.05. - 20.05. |
| Sommer | 17.07. - 27.08. |

Die genannten Tage sind jeweils der erste und letzte Ferientag.

1. *Im Sommer:* _____

2. *Zu Ostern:* _____

3. *Im Herbst:* _____

4. *Zu Pfingsten:* _____

5. *Zu Weihnachten:* _____

6. *Im Winter:* _____

7. How many vacation days are there altogether for the year (including weekends)?

   _____

8. Can you figure out what the English equivalents are for *Herbst, Weihnachten, Ostern, Pfingsten?*

   _____

**17** **Complete the following dialog.**

A:  Komm schnell!

B:  _____

A:  Wir haben gleich Mathe.

B:  _____

A:  Oh, es ist zu Hause.

B:  _____

A:  Du hast doch ein Buch.

B: _____

A:    Dann hole ich mein Buch. Es ist zu Hause.

B: _____

A:    Ich komme zehn Minuten zu spät.

**18** *Wo liegen diese Städte?* **Look at the map of Germany and identify the cities indicated. Some cities are identified as points of reference.**

1. _____    6. _____

2. _____    7. _____

3. _____    8. _____

4. _____    9. _____

5. _____    10. _____

## 19 *Kreuzworträtsel*

### WAAGERECHT

2. Früh am Morgen ist es im Herbst noch ___.

5. In Erdkunde bekommt Vanessa immer eine ___.

7. In Physik bekommt Lisa Bachmeier eine gute ___.

10. Matthias ___ so nervös.

11. ___ für Fächer hast du?

12. Sebastian meint, die Probleme sind ___.

14. Jeden ___, Montag bis Freitag, geht Manuela schon früh zu Vanessa.

16. Matthias' ___ ist zu Hause.

### SENKRECHT

1. ___ ist ein Bundesland in Süddeutschland.

3. Der Bus ___ in zehn Minuten.

4. Manuela findet Biologie ___.

6. Sie ___ Klavier oder hören CDs.

8. Die Schultasche liegt auf dem ___.

9. ___ kommt Manuela zu Vanessa rüber.

12. Herr Schröder ist Vanessas ___.

13. Manuela und Vanessa ___ Schulfreunde vor der Schule.

15. Hat er ___? Nein, das stimmt nicht.

# KAPITEL 5

## Lektion A

**1** *Wie ist das Wetter heute?* **Look at each illustration below and write an appropriate answer to the question.**

1.  _____

2.  _____

3.  _____

4. 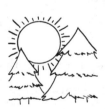 _____

5.  _____

6.  _____

2 **The months of the year are spelled out in the word find below. The letters may go backward or forward; they may go up, down, across or diagonally. However, they go only one way in any one word. Can you find all the months? (Note: Ä=AE)**

M A L A A P L R P G Q A

L Y M A I I L U J I A D

I N G P O U P U L E N T

N O T R J A N U A R O E

L A E I V I E O E A V R

M T Y L A Y R B E U E A

O S E P T E M B E R M N

L U Y N W E O B A B B B

O G N E Z R E A M E E G

H U R E B O T K O F R I

G A D H B L E O W F W R

O A D R S F G N I D M O

Name _____ Datum _____

**3** *In welchem Monat und in welcher Jahreszeit ist...?* Indicate the month and season for each special event listed. *Auf Deutsch, bitte!*

*Beispiel:* Valentine's Day
*Februar, Winter*

1. Washington's birthday: _____

2. Thanksgiving: _____

3. Beginning of the school year: _____

4. Memorial Day: _____

5. Christmas: _____

6. Independence Day: _____

7. Martin Luther King, Jr. Day: _____

8. Columbus Day: _____

9. St. Patrick's Day: _____

10. Your birthday: _____

**4** *Wie ist das Wetter in...?* **Using the information provided in the chart, report what the weather is like in each city. You may wish to use the vocabulary from your book or from the chart. (Some additional useful vocabulary is:** *wolkig* **cloudy;** *heiter* **clear;** *sonnig* **sunny;** *Grad* **degree[s]).**

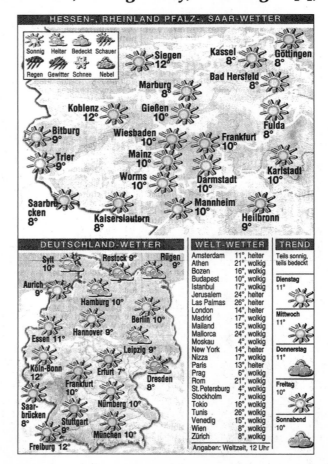

Name _____ Datum _____

*Beispiel:* Berlin
In Berlin ist es 10 Grad und sonnig.

1. München

_____

2. Dresden

_____

3. London

_____

4. Wien

_____

5. Siegen

_____

6. Madrid

_____

7. Rostock

_____

8. Rom

_____

9. Jerusalem

_____

10. Zürich

_____

## 5 Was passt hier? (You won't need all the answers provided.)

_____ 1. Wie ist es im April?

_____ 2. Scheint die Sonne?

_____ 3. Kommst du im Herbst?

_____ 4. Wann kommt der Bus?

_____ 5. Gehen wir schnell!

_____ 6. Was steht auf dem Fahrplan?

A. Immer mit der Ruhe!

B. Ja, morgen.

C. Nein, es regnet.

D. Nicht sehr kalt.

E. Um wie viel Uhr der Bus kommt.

F. Ja, im Oktober.

G. In fünf Minuten.

H. Er kennt sie gut.

## 6 Wo ist...? Using each noun listed, write a question and then answer it.

Beispiel:  Computer
Wo ist ein Computer? Ein Computer ist da.

1. Schule

_____

2. Landkarte

_____

3. Telefon

_____

4. Bleistift

_____

5. Stuhl

_____

6. Bus

_____

**7** **Complete each sentence using a different noun with the appropriate indefinite article.**

1. Petra und Katrin sehen _____ .

2. Kennst du _____ ?

3. Wann holt ihr _____ ?

4. Wir lesen gern _____ .

5. Ich kaufe _____ .

6. Habt ihr _____ ?

7. Sie brauchen _____ .

8. Im Sommer bekomme ich _____ .

**8** *Die Hauptstadt Berlin.* **After reading about Berlin in the *Aktuelles* section, you have become somewhat familiar with Germany's capital city. Select one of the important sights listed at the bottom of the Berlin map (at the front of your textbook) and write a few sentences about it. You may want to use the library or the Internet for information about your topic (Note: You'll find lots of information on this web site: www.berlin.de). You should include the name and location of the sight, its historical significance and a description.**

_____

_____

_____

_____

_____

_____

_____

_____

_____

_____

_____

_____

_____

_____

# KAPITEL 5

## Lektion B

**9** **Wie heißen die Nachbbarländer (1-9) und die Städte (A-H) von Deutschland?**

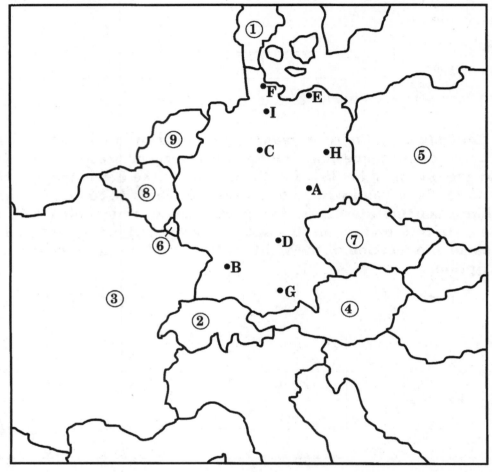

1. _____    A. _____
2. _____    B. _____
3. _____    C. _____
4. _____    D. _____
5. _____    E. _____
6. _____    F. _____
7. _____    G. _____
8. _____    H. _____
9. _____    I. _____

**10** *Welche Sprachen spricht man in diesen Städten?* **Look at the international weather report. For each city listed, name the country and the language spoken. If you don't know the country's name or language in German, give the answer in English.**

## Das Wetter

**Wetterdaten vom Vortag, 14 Uhr MEZ**

|  | **Ausland** |  |  | **Deutschland** |  |
|---|---|---|---|---|---|
| **Ort** | **Wetter** | **Grad** | **Ort** | **Wetter** | **Grad** |
| Amsterdam | Regen | 9 | Berlin | Regen | 10 |
| Athen | leicht bewölkt | 26 | Dresden | Regen | 18 |
| Brüssel | Regen | 9 | Feldberg/Schw. | stark bewölkt | 5 |
| Budapest | wolkig | 25 | Feldberg/Ts. | wolkig | 9 |
| Dublin | wolkig | 8 | Frankfurt/M. | stark bewölkt | 16 |
| Helsinki | stark bewölkt | 5 | Freiburg | wolkig | 17 |
| Innsbruck | wolkig | 20 | Garmisch | bedeckt | 13 |
| Istanbul | wolkenlos | 24 | Hamburg | Regen | 9 |
| London | leicht bewölkt | 11 | Helgoland | Regen | 9 |
| Madrid | wolkig | 12 | Köln/Bonn | stark bewölkt | 14 |
| Mallorca | leicht bewölkt | 21 | Leipzig | stark bewölkt | 14 |
| Moskau | leicht bewölkt | 17 | München | Regen | 13 |
| Paris | Regen | 14 | Norderney | Regen | 9 |
| Tunis | leicht bewölkt | 27 | Rostock | Regen | 10 |
| Venedig | wolkig | 20 | Sylt | stark bewölkt | 7 |
| Warschau | wolkig | 23 | Zugspitze | in Wolken | 0 |
| Wien | wolkig | 24 | | | |
| Zürich | leicht bewölkt | 13 | | | |

*Beispiel:* Mallorca
Spanien, Spanisch

Budapest
*Hungary, Hungarian*

1. Wien _____

2. Moskau _____

3. Helsinki _____

4. Brüssel _____

5. London _____

6. Madrid _____

7. Istanbul _____

8. Zürich _____

9. Venedig _____

10. Warschau _____

11. Athen _____

12. Paris _____

**11** *Wass passt zusammen?* **Match the questions with the appropriate responses.**

_____ 1. Welches Land liegt nicht weit von Flensburg?

_____ 2. Wo liegt Augsburg?

_____ 3. Für wen ist das Fahrrad?

_____ 4. Wie gefällt es dir?

_____ 5. Wen besuchen Sie?

_____ 6. Hast du genug Geld?

_____ 7. Ist es teuer?

_____ 8. Wohin fahren sie?

A. Nein, nicht ganz.

B. Für meinen Bruder.

C. Dänemark.

D. Nach Polen.

E. Im Süden.

F. Meine Schwester.

G. Ja, es ist nicht preiswert.

H. Sehr gut.

**12** **Fill in the plural forms for the nouns listed in parentheses.**

1. Wir kommen in fünf (Minute) _____ rüber.

2. Bringt zwei (Fußball) _____ mit!

3. Warum kaufst du so viele (Buch) _____?

4. In drei (Stunde) _____ beginnt das Rockkonzert.

5. Wie viele (Rechner) _____ braucht ihr denn in Mathe?

6. Angelika hat zwei (Bruder) _____.

7. Haben Sie ein paar (Kuli) _____?

8. In der Stadt gibt es drei (Bahnhof) _____.

9. Peter hat viele (Freundin) _____.

10 Beide (Hemd) _____ sind preiswert.

**13** **Identify each illustration by writing the article and nouns for both singular and plural.**

1. _____

2. _____

3. _____

4. _____

5. _____

6. _____

7. _____

8. _____

9. _____

10. _____

## 14 *Wie viel?* oder *Wie viele?*

1. _____ Lehrer und Lehrerinnen habt ihr?

2. _____ Karten kaufst du für das Konzert?

3. _____ Geld brauchst du? Zehn Euro.

4. _____ Tage bleibt ihr in Innsbruck?

5. _____ kostet der Computer?

6. _____ Zeit haben Sie heute Nachmittag?

7. _____ Freunde bringst du mit?

## 15 Based on the *Lesestück,* find the most appropriate ending for each sentence beginning.

_____ 1. Carsten und Steffen möchten...    A. zur Kasse.

_____ 2. Carstens Fahrrad ist...    B. nicht zu viel.

_____ 3. Im Kaufhaus sind...    C. die Räder heute nicht teuer.

_____ 4. Steffen und Carsten fahren...    D. einen Helm und einen Reifen.

_____ 5. 250 Euro für das Fahrrad ist...    E. nicht mehr neu.

_____ 6. Steffen findet...    F. nicht genug Geld.

_____ 7. Carsten hat...    G. eine Radtour machen.

_____ 8. Steffen braucht...    H. in den Ferien zum Rhein.

_____ 9. Der Helm passt...    I. Steffen gut.

_____ 10. Beide gehen...    J. das Fahrrad nicht schlecht.

**16** **Imagine that you are in a department store talking to a salesperson. Complete the following conversation.**

*Verkäuferin:* Wie gefällt dir dieses Rad?

*Du:* _____

*Verkäuferin:* Es ist heute sehr preiswert.

*Du:* _____

*Verkäuferin:* Nur 180 Euro.

*Du:* _____

*Verkäuferin:* Brauchst du es schon heute?

*Du:* _____

*Verkäuferin:* So? Eine Radtour? Wohin denn?

*Du:* _____

*Verkäuferin:* Wo wohnt denn dein Onkel?

*Du:* _____

*Verkäuferin:* Hast du genug Geld?

*Du:* _____

*Verkäuferin:* Gut, bis später.

**17** ***Was passt hier?*** **Match the words listed below with the words provided**

| | | | | | | |
|---|---|---|---|---|---|---|
| Geld | Jahr | Reifen | Film | Helm | Englisch | |
| Tafel | Tante | Tisch | Jahreszeit | Fußball | Osten | |

1. Stuhl: _____

2. Video: _____

3. Monat: _____

4. Westen: _____

5. Onkel: _____

6. Tennis: _____

7. Deutsch: _____

8. Kreide: _____

9. Rad: _____

10. Herbst: _____

11. Kasse: _____

12. Kopf: _____

Name _____  Datum _____

## 18 Kreuzworträtsel

**WAAGERECHT**

3. Carsten kauft ein ___ im Kaufhaus.

5. Belgien ist ein ___ von Deutschland.

7. Sie ___ an der Kasse.

9. Steffens Reifen ist ___.

12. In dieser Jahreszeit ist es sehr kalt.

13. Das Brandenburger ___

14. Jens' ___ wohnt in Bregenz.

15. Steffen braucht einen ___ und einen Reifen.

16. Das ist ein Monat im Frühling.

17. Die Sonne ___ heute.

**SENKRECHT**

1. Ein Jahr hat zwölf ___.

2. Carsten braucht noch etwas ___.

3. Steffen ___ das Fahrrad sehr gut.

4. Immer mit der ___!

6. Das ___ ist heute sehr schön.

8. Berlin ist die ___ von Deutschland.

10. In der Schweiz sprechen sie ___.

11. Auf dem Fahrplan ___, wann die Busse kommen.

12. Im Juli ist es in Deutschland ___.

# KAPITEL 6

## Lektion A

**1** **Match the questions with the appropriate responses. You will not need all the responses listed.**

_____ 1. Wie schmeckt dir der Sauerbraten?

_____ 2. Was isst du mit deinem Hamburger?

_____ 3. Möchtest du mitkommen?

_____ 4. Wo treffen wir sie?

_____ 5. Gehen nur drei dorthin?

_____ 6. Wann gibt's Mittagessen?

_____ 7. Was ist eine Kalte Platte?

_____ 8. Was ist auf dem Brötchen?

_____ 9. Um wie viel Uhr esst ihr das Abendessen?

_____ 10. Wohin gehst du?

A. Um halb eins.

B. Nach Hause.

C. Nicht besonders.

D. Beim Imbiss.

E. Butter und Marmelade.

F. Ja, gern.

G. Wurst und Käse.

H. So gegen sieben.

I. Ja, aber wir treffen noch andere.

J. Pommes frites.

Name _____ Datum _____

## 2 Deutsche Restaurants.
The following restaurant ads are from Miltenberg, located in southern Germany. Answer the following questions in German and give the English equivalent in parentheses following each answer.

Für Sie serviert ...

Konditorei-Café
**Bauer**
An der alten Domkellerei
Miltenberg

Hauptstraße 41
Miltenberg
Telefon 0 93 71 / 23 84

Hotel-Gasthof
**Hopfengarten**
Räume für Festlichkeiten aller Art
Ankergasse 16 • Miltenberg
Telefon (0 93 71) 31 31 • Fax 6 97 58

hauseigener
Tennisplatz
Fremdenzimmer

Wenschdorf
Tel. (0 93 71) 36 23

Gasthaus zum Hirschen
Fam. Farrenkopf

Griechische und deutsche Spezialitäten
Hotel
**Gasthaus Frühlingsgarten**
Tagungsräume bis 30 Personen
Alle Zimmer mit Dusche und WC
**0 93 71 / 21 15**
Eichenbühler Straße 72 • Miltenberg
Öffnungszeiten: Tägl. 11.00 –14.00 + 18.00 –1.00 Uhr

**Pinocchio**
Ristorante - Pizzeria
Mainstr. 47 • Miltenberg • Tel. (0 93 71) 8 04 50

schnell ... preiswert ... gut
**Odenwald Grill**
Fußgängerzone Miltenberg
Tel. (0 93 71) 37 08
Öffnungszeiten: 10.00 – 20.00 Uhr
Kein Ruhetag • ganztags warme Küche
Straßenverkauf
• Alle Speisen gut verpackt auch zum Mitnehmen!

*Beispiel:*  Do you have to wait long to get served at *Odenwald Grill?*
*Nein, es geht schnell.* (No, it's fast.)

1. What ethnic specialties does *Gasthaus Frühlingsgarten* offer?

_____

_____

2. What type of food is served at *Pinocchio?*

_____

3. Do you have to eat all the meals at the restaurant *Odenwald Grill?*

_____

_____

4. What number would you call if you wanted to reach the *Hopfengarten* from outside the city of Miltenberg?

_____

5. Besides being a restaurant, *Gasthaus Frühlingsgarten* also offers sleeping accommodations. What do all the rooms have?

_____

_____

6. What kind of eating establishment is *Bauer,* and what type of food does it offer?

_____

_____

7. What are the restaurant hours for *Odenwald Grill?*

_____

8. What's the local phone number for *Konditorei-Café Bauer?*

_____

**3** *Was passt hier?* **Find the eight words that will combine to form new words (compound nouns). Use each syllable only once.**

| | | | | | |
|---|---|---|---|---|---|
| BISS | BRA | BROT | BUR | DE | ER |
| ES | FRÜH | GER | GER | HAM | HUN |
| IM | KÄ | LA | MAR | ME | MIT |
| SAU | SE | SEN | STÜCK | TAG | TEN |

1. _____

2. _____

3. _____

4. _____

5. _____

6. _____

7. _____

8. _____

**4** **Complete the following dialog by filling in the appropriate form of these modals:** *möchten, müssen, wollen.* **You may be able to use more than one of these modals for each sentence.**

*Dieter:* _____ du einen Hamburger?

*Katrin:* Ich _____ nur Pommes frites.

*Dieter:* Uwe _____ später zu mir rüberkommen. Wir

_____ die Deutschaufgaben machen.

_____ du auch kommen?

Katrin: Nein, ich _____ zu Hause bleiben. Ich habe viel

zu tun.

*Dieter:* _____ du denn die ganze Zeit zu Hause sein?

Katrin: Nein, das nicht, aber heute Abend _____ ich

einen tollen Film im Fernsehen sehen.

**5** **Write the proper form of the modals given in parentheses.**

1. (Mögen) _____ er die Wurst nicht?

2. (Wollen) _____ Sie heute Nachmittag in die Stadt gehen?

3. Ich (möchten) _____ meine Cousine besuchen.

4. (Müssen) _____ ihr denn die ganze Arbeit machen?

5. (Möchten) _____ du diesen tollen Krimi lesen?

6. Natascha (müssen) _____ ein Buch lesen.

7. Wir (mögen) _____ das nicht essen.

8. Ich (wollen) _____ morgen zu meinem Freund fahren.

9. (Möchten) _____ ihr einen Hamburger oder eine Bratwurst?

10 Renate (wollen) _____ gleich mit Gisela sprechen.

**6** Complete the following dialog by filling in the appropriate forms of these modals: *können, möchten, müssen, wollen.* You may be able to use more than one modal form for each sentence.

Heinz:   Du, Christa, _____ du morgen ins Rockkonzert

gehen?

Christa:  Nein, Heinz. Ich _____ nicht. Ich

_____ bis dann noch ein Buch lesen.

Heinz:   Das _____ ich auch tun.

Christa:  Ich _____ meine Arbeit heute machen.

Heinz:   _____ du später rüberkommen?

Christa:  Ich _____ schon, aber heute geht es wirklich nicht.

**7** *Was ist das?* Identify each word in English.

1. Trinkgeld: _____

2. Wirt: _____

3. Gedeck: _____

4. Leitungswasser: _____

5. Rechnung: _____

6. Mehrwertsteuer: _____

7. Speisekarte: _____

8. Bedienung: _____

# KAPITEL 6

## Lektion B

**8** *Welches Wort fehlt?* **Complete each phrase using the appropriate verb from the list. You may use each verb only once.**

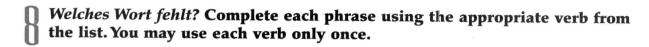

haben    essen    trinken    kosten        gehen    fahren
    treffen            sein

1. eine Tasse Kaffee _____

2. in die Pizzeria _____

3. lieber ein Nusseis _____

4. Freunde vor der Pizzeria _____

5. viel Geld _____

6. einen großen Durst _____

7. das Eiscafé zu weit _____

8. mit dem Auto in die Ferien _____

**9** *Wie viel kostet das?* Look at the German menu below and answer this question based on the various situations. (Vocabulary: *ein Stück* a piece; *preiswertest-* most reasonable; *teuerst-* most expensive.)

| **Warme Getränke** | | **Eisspezialitäten** | |
|---|---|---|---|
| Tasse Kaffee | € 1,20 | Erdbeereis mit Schlagsahne | € 2,40 |
| Kännchen Kaffee | € 3,20 | Vanilleeis | € 1,90 |
| Espresso | € 2,10 | Schokoeis | € 1,90 |
| Glas Tee | € 1,60 | Gemischtes Eis | € 3,40 |
| Tasse Kakao | € 2,80 | Große Portion Eis mit | |
| **Kalte Getränke** | | Früchten | € 4,20 |
| Cola | € 2,00 | **Kuchen und Torten** | |
| Fanta | € 2,00 | Sachertorte | € 1,90 |
| Spezi | € 1,80 | Schwarzwälder Kirschtorte | € 2,10 |
| Apfelsaft | € 1,70 | Apfelstrudel | € 1,60 |
| Orangensaft | € 1,60 | Nusstorte | € 1,80 |
| Mineralwasser | € 1,40 | | |
| Tonic | € 2,40 | | |

1. ein Kännchen Kaffee und ein Stück Apfelstrudel

   _____

2. ein Schokoeis, Erdbeereis mit Schlagsahne und eine Cola

   _____

3. eine Fanta, zwei Colas, ein Apfelsaft, eine Große Portion Eis

   _____

4. eine Portion von allen Eisspezialitäten

   _____

5. drei Stück Schwarzwälder Kirschtorte, ein Stück Nusstorte, ein Gemischtes Eis, drei Tassen Kaffee, ein Apfelsaft und ein Orangensaft

   _____

6. das preiswerteste Getränk

   _____

7. das teuerste Eis

   _____

Name _____ Datum _____

**10** *Eiscafés.* **Below you'll see several cafés in the city of Aachen. Find the answers to the following questions. (Some words you may want to know are:** *die Kugel* **scoop;** *geöffnet* **open.) Which café...**

## eis

*War man früher mit der Frage „Vanille, Erdbeer oder Schoko" beschäftigt, tun sich heute zwischen A wie „After-Eight-Becher" und Z wie „Zimteis" unendliche Wahlmöglichkeiten auf. Nur eine Frage ist gleichgeblieben: Waffel oder Becher? Hier die nötigen Adressen.*

**Willi Delzepich**
Adalbertsteinweg 236 /Eingang
Bismarckstr.
52066 Aachen
☎ 50 04 92
Tägl. 7-18.30 h, Sa 9-13.30 h
*Willi Delzepich verkauft nicht nur Eis, er stellt es auch selbst her. Bereits in der 3. Generation bietet die Aachener Eislegende seine Köstlichkeiten an. 1984 erhielt Öko-Willi den 1. Umweltpreis in Aachen: Die Einführung der Flaschenmilch z.B. geht auf seine Kappe. Wer in Aachen Urlaub macht oder hier wohnt, muß unbedingt bei ihm gewesen sein.*

**Al Teatro**
Kapuzinergraben 2a
52062 Aachen
☎ 3 86 77
Mo-Fr 10-24, So
11.30-24 Uhr
*Klassisches italienisches Eis, die Kugeln sind etwas größer als normal und kosten € -.50.*

**Eiscafé Napoli**
Adalbertsteinweg 14
52070 Aachen
☎ 50 26 81
Tägl. 10-22 h
*Angeboten werden 22 Eissorten aus eigener Produktion. Für Unersättliche gibt es den Big-Becher für € 5. Eis ohne Ende mit Früchten und Soßen bis zum Abwinken.*

**Tutto Gelato**
Büchel 16
52062 Aachen
☎ 3 52 00
Täglich 11-23 h
*Kleiner Laden riesiges Eissortiment. Keine Tische und Stühle, das Eis gibt's auf die Hand. Die Kugel kostet €*

**Eis-Café Dolomiti**
Morlaixplatz 4
52146 Würselen
☎ 0 24 05 / 1 89 27
Täglich 9.30 - 22.00 Uhr
*Giovanni Merlo bietet Eis-Spezialitäten (eigene Herstellung, Kugel € -.50, Longdrinks, Milch-Shakes, kalte und warme Getränke. Bis 11 h kann man auch frühstücken. Zum Kaffee schmeckt „heiße Waffel mit Kirschen" oder „Apfelstrudel mit Vanillesoße".*

**Gamba**
Franzstraße 45
52064 Aachen
☎ 3 59 93
Täglich 9.30 bis 23.30 h
*Von Ende Februar bis Mitte Oktober geöffnet. Im Sommer werden hier gerne Früchtebecher gekauft.*

**Del Negro**
Jakobstraße 73 a
52064 Aachen
☎ 2 97 24
Täglich 10-23 h
*Gelegentlich im Sommer, wenn viel zu tun ist, wird auch schon mal länger gearbeitet. Das Del Negro hat 11 Tische innerhalb der Eisdiele, am Wochenende auch 7 Tische außerhalb. Das Angebot umfaßt 26 Eissorten.*

**Frigo**
Peterstraße 13
52062 Aachen
☎ 2 96 33
Tägl. 9.30-23 Uhr
*Hier gibt es viele eisige Raffinessen, beispielsweise den „Gondola Becher" oder das „Pfirsich Melba". Und für Diabetiker ist auch gesorgt. Außerdem gibt's Milchmix' und Frappés unterschiedlicher Geschmacksrichtungen, auf die Kleinen wartet das „Pinocchio Eis" und die Eis-„Biene Maja".*

**Da Piano**
Kapellenstraße 21
52066 Aachen
☎ 6 55 88
Täglich 9-22.30, So 10-22.30
*Von März bis Oktober geöffnet, Unheimlich große Auswahl: 42 Sorten Eis.*

**Roncaletti**
Bahnhofstraße 22
52064 Aachen
☎ 40 61 85
Mo-Fr 10-23, Sa/So 12-23 h
*Von Anfang Februar bis November/Dezember geöffnet, besondere Spezialität: Joghurt mit vielen Früchten, im Sommer auch schon mal länger bis 1 Uhr geöffnet*

1. ...doesn't have any tables?

_____

2. ...specializes in Italian ice creams, with scoops that are bigger than normal?

_____

3. ...is closed in January?

_____

4. ...offers breakfast service until 11 A.M.?

_____

5. ...has a total of 18 tables (inside and outside) on weekends?

   _____

6. ...offers the largest assortment of ice creams?

   _____

7. ...has its establishment and café entrance on *Bismarkstraße?*

   _____

8. ...is open daily from 9:30 A.M. to 11:30 P.M.?

   _____

9. ...offers ice cream for diabetics?

   _____

10. ...sells a large dish of ice cream for five euro?

   _____

## 11 Complete each sentence using the appropriate form of *werden*.

1. Wann _____ ihr uns besuchen?

2. Wir _____ am Freitag kommen.

3. Wie viele CDs _____ du im Kaufhaus kaufen?

4. Ich _____ zwei CDs kaufen.

5. _____ Sonja im Sommer nach Europa fahren?

6. Ja, sie und ihre Freundin Monika _____ dorthin fahren.

7. Wo _____ Sie auch mich warten, Frau Krüger?

8. Ich _____ bei der Videothek auf Sie warten.

## 12 You are disagreeing with what is being said. Say the opposite of what you hear.

*Beispiele:* Sie hat eine Freundin.
Sie hat keine Freundin.

Ich sage das nicht.
Ich sage das.

1. Boris kauft ein Buch.

   _____

2. Katja lernt Mathe.

   _____

3. Sie sind nicht sehr froh.

   _____

4. Wir haben keine Zeit.

   _____

5. Herr Meier ist zu Hause.

   _____

6. Der Film ist nicht besonders gut.

   _____

7. Ich kenne keinen Lehrer.

   _____

8. Susi hat viel Geld.

   _____

9. Ich habe eine Landkarte.

   _____

10. Sie haben nicht viel zu tun.

    _____

## 13 Answer these questions in the negative.

1. Isst du Zitroneneis gern?

   _____

2. Gehst du heute Nachmittag in die Stadt?

   _____

3. Möchtest du ein Klavier kaufen?

   _____

4. Trinkst du eine Tasse Kaffee?

   _____

5. Kommst du um zwei nach Hause?

   _____

6. Beginnt das Fernsehprogramm um halb sieben Uhr?

   _____

7. Kennst du alle in deiner Klasse sehr gut?

   _____

8. Willst du einen Onkel besuchen?

   _____

**14** ***Was fehlt hier?*** **Fill in the proper forms of the verbs listed below based on the** *Lesestück.*

| | | | | | |
|---|---|---|---|---|---|
| machen | sein | kommen | bezahlen | möchten | dauern |
| fahren | sprechen | sollen | schicken | treffen | sitzen |
| schreiben | bleiben | werden | bringen | schmecken | |

Tobias und seine Freunde _____ nach der Schule mit ihren

Fahrrädern zu einem Eiscafé. Dort _____ sie oft Schulfreunde. Es

_____ heute etwas kühl, aber sie _____ doch

lieber draußen an einem Tisch.


Bald _____ der Kellner. Karin _____ einen

Schokoshake und Sarah eine Eisschokolade. Der Kellner _____

aber für Gülten einen Erdbeershake und für Tobias ein Spaghetti Eis bringen.

Der Kellner _____ auch alles schon bald. Das Eis

_____ Tobias besonders gut.


Sarah und ihre Eltern _____ im Sommer zur Insel Rügen fahren.

Gülten wird aber im Sommer vielleicht zu Hause _____ .

_____ Gülten ihrem Cousin einen Brief? Nein, das

_____ zu lange, bis er da ist. Deshalb _____ sie

eine E-Mail. Karin _____ auch nichts in den Ferien. Alle vier

_____ noch viel über die Ferien. Dann _____ sie

für die Leckerbissen und fahren nach Hause.

**15** *Was möchten alle und wie viel kostet es?* The Neubergers are traveling with three other couples to the Nürnberg area in southern Germany. They have just gone into a restaurant to order lunch. Everyone has a different idea about what he or she wants to eat.

Look at the menu. The numbers before the various meals indicate who is ordering what. Note that some order more than one dish. In the space provided, write the names of the dishes and the cost for each person. The English equivalent for the main categories are: *Suppen* soups; *Für den kleinen Hunger* for the small appetite; *Hauptgerichte* entrees, main meals; *Hausspezialitäten* house specialties; *Getränke* beverages (Note: *Spezi* = cola and lemon soda). Here is a list of what everyone is ordering:

❶ **Herr Neuberger**  ❺ **Herr Rubinski**
❷ **Frau Neuberger**  ❻ **Frau Rubinski**
❸ **Herr Sternke**  ❼ **Herr Albrecht**
❹ **Frau Sternke**  ❽ **Frau Albrecht**

## Vorspeisen    €

Geräuchertes Forellenfilet mit Apfelkren,
Toast und Butter    6,75
Homesmoked Troutfilet with Horseradish, Toast and Butter

Tellerfleisch von der Ochsenbrust mit
Schnittlauchmarinade, Brot und Butter    6,25
Sliced Breast of Beef with Chive-Garlic Dressing, Bread and Butter

Großer Salatteller mit gebratener Entenburst    8,75
Large Salad Plate with Breast of Duckling

"Obatzter" mit Radi und Brezeln (angemachter
Camembert)    6,75
"Obatzter" (Specially seasoned Camembert with "Radi" and Pretzel)

## Suppen    €

Hühnerbrühe ❸ ❻    2,90
Chicken Broth

Kartoffelsuppe ❹    3,00
Potato Soup

Leberknödelsuppe ❶ ❼    3,25
Liver Dumpling Soup

Hausgemachte Goulaschsuppe ❷ ❽    3,40
Homemade Goulash Soup

## Für den kleinen Hunger    €

2 Stück Weißwürste mit Brot ❷    4,00
2 White Sausages wiht Bavarian Mustard, Bread

Nürnberger Stadtwurst ❽    4,25
Bratwurst "Nürnberg Style"

Gebackener Camembert    5,00
Baked Camembert

Hausgemachte Käs'spätzle ❹    6,75
Homemade Cheese-Spätzle

Nürnberger Leberknödel    5,60
Liver Dumpling "Nürnberg Style"

## Hauptgerichte    €

Schweinsbraten    8,90
Roasted Pork

Schnitzel "Wiener Art"    9,90
Veal Cutlet "Viennese Style"

Jägerschnitzel ❶    11,60
Cutlet "Hunters Style" with Mushrooms

Kalbsleber ❻    11,60
Calf's Liver

## Hausspezialitäten    €

Rheinischer Sauerbraten ❸    10,75
Marinated Beef

Berliner Eisbein, Sauerkraut und Salzkartoffeln    10,75
Pickled Leg of Pork, Sauerkraut and Boiled Potatoes

Zwiebelrostbraten und grüne Bohnen ❺    12,75
Roast Beef with Onions and Green Beans

Schlachterplatte    11,25
Variety Meat Plate

## Getränke    €

Cola ❶ ❺ ❽    1,75

Mineralwasser ❷ ❹ ❻    1,60

Spezi ❸    1,75

Apfelsaft ❼    2,00

*Beispiel:* Herr Neuberger
Herr Neuberger möchte Leberknödelsuppe, Jägerschnitzel und eine Cola. Es kostet € 16,60 (16 Euro, 60 Cent).

1. Frau Neuberger

_____

_____

_____

2. Herr Sternke

_____

_____

_____

3. Frau Sternke

_____

_____

_____

4. Herr Rubinski

_____

_____

_____

5. Frau Rubinski

_____

_____

_____

6. Herr Albrecht

_____

_____

_____

7. Frau Albrecht

_____

_____

_____

**16** **Form compound nouns by adding nouns from the list to the existing ones. Note that the article in the newly formed noun may change and that some letters may have to be added or deleted to complete each new word. Once you have found the new noun, write a sentence using it in context.**

| das Brot | das Land | die Sahne | der Saft | das Essen |
|----------|----------|-----------|----------|-----------|
| die Schau | die Zeit | die Karte | der Shake | die Aufgabe |

*Beispiel:* der Mittag
das Mittagessen
Wir essen Mittagessen um halb eins.

1. die Erdbeere: _____

   _____

2. der Abend: _____

   _____

3. der Apfel: _____

   _____

4. der Sport: _____

   _____

5. der Schlag: _____

   _____

6. das Land: _____

   _____

7. die Wurst: _____

   _____

8. das Jahr: _____

   _____

9. der Nachbar: _____

   _____

10. das Haus: _____

   _____

Name _____ Datum _____

**17** *Weißt du die Antworten?* **Identify each noun described. You will find most of the answers in this chapter of your textbook. The first letters of the nouns, when read in sequence, pay you a compliment.**

1.  Sabrina sagt, sie möchte nichts trinken. Sie hat keinen _____.

2.  Wie viel _____ ist es denn? Es ist schon halb fünf.

3.  Zum Frühstück essen das viele Deutsche auf dem Brot oder Brötchen mit Marmelade. _____

4.  Monika und Emine wollen dort etwas essen. _____

5.  Er geht mit Monika und Emine dorthin. Wie heißt er? _____

6.  Gültens Cousin wohnt in diesem Land. _____

7.  Man trinkt Milch oder Cola daraus *(out of it)*. _____

8.  Das trinken viele gern. Es ist kalt und kommt oft in einem Glas.
    _____

9.  Das ist Frankreich von Deutschland. _____

10. Ein Eis. Es ist aber kein Schokoeis, Vanilleeis oder Erdbeereis.
    _____

11. Er bringt Karin, Sarah, Gülten und Tobias alle Leckerbissen in einem Eiscafé.
    _____

12. Tobias isst Spaghetti Eis. Es ist Tobias' _____.

13. Wann beginnt der Krimi im Fernsehen? Um acht _____.

14. Sie mag Schokolade nicht._____

# 18 Kreuzworträtsel (Note: Ö = OE, Ü = UE, ß = SS)

## WAAGERECHT

1. Soll ich Ihnen ein ___ Apfelsaft oder eine Tasse Kaffee bringen?

4. __ schön? Ich möchte eine Bratwurst bitte.

6. Der ___ bringt alle Leckerbissen.

7. Guten ___! Schmeckt's gut?

10. Was für ___ möchten Sie? Vanille und Schoko.

12. Bringen Sie mir bitte ein Wiener ___!

## SENKRECHT

2. Möchtet ihr Schokoeis? Nein, wir essen ___ Nusseis.

3. Bringen Sie bitte Bratwurst mit Kartoffeln und ___.

4. Schickst du eine E-Mail oder einen ___?

5. Wir sitzen heute lieber ___ im Café. Die Sonne scheint und es ist so warm.

8. Was ___ du zum Frühstück? Ich habe keinen Hunger.

**WAAGERECHT**

13. Was willst du ___? Ein Glas , Apfelsaft bitte.

15. Ich esse gern ___ frites mit einem Hamburger.

17. ___ ihr nicht bald gehen? Oh ja, es ist schon zehn vor acht.

19. Möchtest du eine Scheibe Brot oder ein ___?

20. Was machst du am Sonntag? ___.

**SENKRECHT**

9. Zum ___ gibt es Kalte Platte.

11. Hast du heute Nachmittag Zeit? Nein, ___ nicht.

14. Wie viel ___ der Erdbeershake? Nur zwei Euro.

16. Trinkst du Cola oder ___?

18. Hast du ___? Ja, ich möchte eine Cola.

## 19  *Was möchtest du?* Assume that you are working in a café. Write your responses when conversing with the two different customers.

*Du:* _____

*Dame:* Ich möchte ein Zitroneneis.

*Du:* _____

*Dame:* Ja, ein Schokoshake.

*Du:* _____

*Dame:* Eine Tasse Kaffee und einen Eistee, bitte.

*Du:* _____

*Dame:* Das kostet aber viel Geld.

*Du:* _____

\*\*\*

*Herr:* Ich habe Durst.

*Du:* _____

*Herr:* Was schmeckt denn gut?

*Du:* _____

*Herr:* Wie viel kostet ein Glas Cola?

*Du:* _____

*Herr:* Ich möchte auch etwas essen.

*Du:* _____

*Herr:* Eine Bratwurst mit Brot.

*Du:* _____

*Herr:* Nein, danke.

# KAPITEL 7

## Lektion A

**1** **Was passt hier?**

_____ 1. Was hat sie an?

_____ 2. Wie ist das Kleid?

_____ 3. Passt die Hose?

_____ 4. Gefällt dir der Pulli?

_____ 5. Wie findest du das
      Sonderangebot?

_____ 6. Gibt es da eine große Auswahl?

_____ 7. Wie ist die Qualität drinnen?

_____ 8. Was kauft er denn?

A. Nein, sie haben nur ein paar
   Sachen.

B. Zu eng.

C. Er kauft ein Hemd und eine
   Krawatte.

D. Eine Bluse.

E. Die Preise sind sehr gut.

F. Viel besser. Hier draußen ist
   alles viel zu billig.

G. Nicht besonders. Er ist auch zu
   groß.

H. Nein, sie ist zu klein.

**2** *Wie heißen diese Kleidungsstücke?* **Write the singular and plural forms of
the clothing items illustrated. Include the articles as well.**

1. _____

2. _____

3. _____

4. _____

5. _____

6. _____

7. _____

8. _____

9. _____

10. _____

11. _____

12. _____

Name _____ Datum _____

**3** *Da ist alles billiger!* Look at the ad and answer the questions in complete sentences. (Note: *Lagerverkauf* warehouse sale; *ist geöffnet* is open)

**LAGERVERKAUF**

Jede Woche
Mi. – Fr.
11-17 Uhr

*Exclusive Damenmode*

**Markenware zu Fabrikpreisen**

**Röcke/Hosen** ..ab EURO **24,–**
**Blazer** ...........ab EURO **49,–**
**Jacken** ...........ab EURO **99,–**
**Kostüme** ........ab EURO **99,–**
**Mäntel** ..........ab EURO **109,–**

**Mode Magazin** Großbeeren, Gewerbegebiet (GVZ)
Hauptstraße 14-16 • Telefon: 033701–2 28 00

1. Für wie viel Geld kann man einen Mantel kaufen?

   _____

2. Wie heißt die Stadt, wo der Lagerverkauf ist?

   _____

3. In welcher Straße ist das Mode Magazin?

   _____

4. An welchen drei Tagen gibt es hier den Lagerverkauf?

   _____

5. Wie ist die Telefonnummer vom Mode Magazin?

   _____

6. Wie viele Stunden in der Woche ist Mode Magazin geöffnet?

   _____

**4** **Put together the syllables below to form German words for the following items. Each syllable may be used only once.**

| AN | BLU | HAND | HE | HO | KRA |
|----|-----|------|----|----|-----|
| LI | MAN | PUL | SCHU | SCHUH | SE |
| SE | TE | TEL | WAT | ZUG | |

1. *coat:* _____

2. *tie:* _____

3. *glove:* _____

4. *suit:* _____

5. *sweater:* _____

6. *pants:* _____

7. *shoes:* _____

8. *blouse:* _____

**5** **Fill in the appropriate forms of the verbs given in parentheses.**

1. Der Pulli (gefallen) _____ mir nicht.

2. (lesen) _____ du diesen Krimi bis morgen?

3. Wir (sehen) _____ diesen Film am Sonntag.

4. (fahren) _____ du später in die Stadt?

5. (gefallen) _____ Ihnen das Buch nicht?

6. Robert (sprechen) _____ englisch, deutsch und französisch.

7. Ich (geben) _____ dir gern zehn Euro.

8. Jana (nehmen) _____ das Shirt nicht. Es ist zu groß für sie.

9. (sehen) _____ du nicht gern fern?

10. Am Morgen (lesen) _____ Herr Krüger immer, was es neues gibt.

11. (geben) _____ es heute Abend Kalte Platte?

12. Warum (essen) _____ ihr den Sauerbraten nicht?

Name _____ Datum _____

**6** *Preiswerte Kleidungsstücke.* **Look at the following ad and then answer the questions.**

## Herbst-Impressionen

## Bekleidunghaus Holtex

### Damen-Mode

**Super praktisch**
**Membranen-Jacke**
wasserdicht, winddicht,
neues Oberstoffmaterial

**59.95**

**Selbstverständlich Stretch**
**Markenhosen**
elegante Webkaros,
Schurwolle-/Polyester-
Qualität

**34.95**

**Wieder eingetroffen!**
**Blusen-Jacke**
in Velourslederoptik,
in vier Farben,
bis Größe 52

**49.95**

**Sehr hochwertige**
**Webpelz-Westen**
mollig warm,
fünf verschiedene Dessins

**99.95**

**Neue Microqualität**
**Longjacke**
webpelzverbrämt an
Kragen und Ärmeln,
Winterfutter, Knopfver-
schluss, Farben:
Bronze und Graphit

**94.95**

### Herren-Mode

**Aktuelle**
**Pullover**
mit Rundhals,
sportliche Dessin,
Farbe: Schwarzmeliert,
maschinenwaschbar

**14.95**

**Bequeme**
**Stretch-Cordhose**
mit elastischem Bund
und Gürtel,
verschiedene Farben,
maschinenwaschbar

**29.95**

**Klassische**
**Kombi-Hose**
mit Bundfalte,
zwei Gesäßtaschen,
60% Schurwolle/
40% Polyester,
maschinenwaschbar

**39.95**

**Sportliche**
**Micro-Moss-Longjacke**
mit Taillenzug und
Zwei-Wege-Taschen,
aktuelle Herbstfarben,
maschinenwaschbar

**44.95**

**Velourslederoptik**
**Thermo-Longjacke**
Tunnelzugform mit
Zwei-Wege-Taschen,
Steh- und Umlegekragen,
maschinenwaschbar

**59.95**

**Hochwertige**
***SYMPATEX***
**Wolljacke**
in verschiedenen Formen
und Farben,
Wolle/Polyester

**94.95**

**Holtex in Flensburg**
**Husumer Straße**
Tel. 04 61 / 9 30 51

**Holtex in Rendsburg**
**Friedrichstädter Straße**
Tel. 04 33 1 / 49 01

**Holtex in Heide/Wesseln**
**Husumer Straße**
Tel. 04 81 / 75 38

**Montag bis Freitag:**
**9.30-19.00 Uhr**
**Samstag: 9.00-16.00 Uhr**

**P Kostenlose Parkplätze vorhanden! P**

1. What would you pay to purchase three pullovers?

   _____

2. In how many cities do you find a Holtex clothing store?

   _____

3. How many hours is Holtex open on Saturdays?

   _____

4. What is the polyester content in the *Kombi-Hose?*

   _____

5. What time of the year does this sale take place?

   _____

6. What material is the *Wolljacke* made of?

_____

7. What is the cost of a *Markenhose, Thermo-Longjacke* and a *Stretch-Cordhose?*

_____

8. What is the local phone number of the Holtex store in Rendsburg?

_____

**7** **State the German name for each description. The words (without articles), when read in sequence, give you a clue as to where you can go shopping in a German city.**

1. fourth floor in Germany

_____

2. suit worn by a male

_____

3. special sales items

_____

4. where you pay for purchased items

_____

5. selection

_____

6. downstairs floor in a department store

_____

7. moving platform that can transport a person with a physical disability to the next floor

_____

8. where you would find such items as pots and pans

_____

9. time of day when German stores are closed

_____

10. what some Germans still believe about purchasing frozen foods

_____

11. what you need to wear on your foot

_____

# KAPITEL 7

## Lektion B

**8** *Was sind die typischen Farben?* **Name the typical colors described below.** *Auf Deutsch, bitte!*

1. color between white and black, ash-colored

   _____

2. color between yellow and red in the spectrum; an edible citrus fruit

   _____

3. dark shade with yellowish or reddish hue; sunburned or tanned skin

   _____

4. adjacent hues in the spectrum such as scarlet, vermillion or cherry; loss or deficit in financial statements

   _____

5. color of growing foliage

   _____

6. without brightness or color; totally dark

   _____

7. light tint of crimson, pale reddish purple; typical color of carnations

   _____

8. color of pure snow

   _____

9. pure hue of clear sky; deep azure

   _____

10. very light brown, grayish tan or sandy color

   _____

## 9 Unscramble the following letters. Each word is the name of a color.

1. L G B E _____
2. S I S W E _____
3. N R B U A _____
4. O R T _____
5. C A S W Z H R _____
6. R G Ü N _____
7. A O R S _____
8. L U A B _____
9. O E A N G R _____

## 10 Was passt hier?

_____ 1. Wie ist die Jacke?

_____ 2. Steht es mir?

_____ 3. Geh doch zur Kasse!

_____ 4. Welche Farbe gefällt dir?

_____ 5. Weißt du, ob er teuer ist?

_____ 6. Warum nimmst du das Paar
Schuhe?

_____ 7. Kauf das doch!

_____ 8. Ist es nicht zu hell?

A. Nein, es ist wirklich zu dunkel.

B. Es ist sehr preiswert.

C. Blau oder rot.

D. Wo ist sie denn?

E. Ich habe nicht genug Geld.

F. Na, billig ist er nicht.

G. Ganz schick.

H. Ja, es passt dir auch gut.

## 11 *Was wissen sie?* Complete each sentence by providing the proper form of *wissen.*

1. Maria und Heinz _____ nicht, wann sie rüberkommen.

2. _____ du, wie viel Uhr es ist?

3. Ich _____, wer das ist.

4. _____ Sie, Frau Rabe, wo der Computer ist?

5. _____ ihr, woher Paul kommt?

6. Wir _____, wo diese Städte liegen.

7. Herr und Frau Krause _____, wo das Kaufhaus ist.

8. Heike _____, wo Holger wohnt.

## 12 *Etwas stimmt hier nicht.* **Rewrite the following incorrect sentences, basing your answers on the** *Lesestück*.

1. Jens und Wolf fahren mit Fahrrädern in die Stadt.

   _____

2. Wolfs Jeans sind ganz neu.

   _____

3. Sie gehen in ein Kaufhaus.

   _____

4. Wolf macht eine Ferienreise.

   _____

5. Wolf fährt im Winter.

   _____

6. Der Schwarzwald liegt im Schluchsee.

   _____

7. Wolf bezahlt nicht ganz 40 Dollar für die Jeans.

   _____

# 13 Create a dialog in German based on the following information.

You and your friend have a lot of time this afternoon and are wondering what to do. You both have several suggestions. Finally, you decide to go shopping. You discuss the alternatives of shopping close by or at a big department store in town. You decide to go to the big department store.

At the store, both of you are interested in a pair of jeans. You ask the salesperson some questions (size, color, price, etc.) and eventually you try them on. You decide to buy the jeans, but your friend wants to shop around some more. You go to the cashier's counter and pay for the jeans.

_____

_____

_____

_____

_____

_____

_____

_____

_____

_____

_____

_____

_____

_____

_____

_____

_____

_____

Name _____  Datum _____

**10 Jahre**
# Mode Ruoff
**in 85072 Eichstätt, Weißenburger Str. 13**

| | | | |
|---|---|---|---|
| **Herren -** **Flanell - Hemden** 100% Baumwolle € 10,- | *Seidensticker* **Herren - Hemden** Baumwolle aktuelle Dessins € 10,- | **Damen - Shirts** **u. Sweat - Shirts** alles aktuelle Modelle aus dieser Saisaon! € 10,- | **Damen- u. Herren-** **Nappalederjacken** hochwertiges Nappaleder schwarz € 150,- |
| **Herren** **Trachten - Hemden** 100 Baumwolle, mit Stickerei weiß, Gr. 39-44 € 10,- | **Herren - Sweat -** **Shirt** versch. Modelle und Dessins, Baumwolle € 10,- | **Kinder - Sweat -** **Shirts** mit Motivdrucken, Gr. 98-184 € 10,- | **Damen - Pullis** verschiedene aktuelle Farben e 10,- |
| **Kleinkinder -** **Nicki - Pullis** teilweise bestickt Gr. 98-118 € 10,- | **Herren - Velourleder -** **Trachtenjanker** Lammvelour mit Stickeri € 198,- | **Kleinkinder-** **Unterziehrolli** Baumwolle versch. Farben Gr. 98 - € 118 5,- | **Damen -** **Strickstrumpfhosen** Kurzgrüßen, Baumwolle oder Wolle € 10,- |

**Mode Ruoff — bequem und preiswert einkaufen! Parkplätze vor der Tür!**

1. Wie alt ist dieses Geschäft?

_____

2. In welcher Stadt ist es?

_____

3. Welche Farbe sind die Herren-Trachten-Hemden?

_____

4. In welchen Größen gibt es sie?

_____

5. Wie viel kosten Damen-Shirts?

_____

6. Gibt es Damen-Pullis nur in einer Farbe?

_____

7. Welche Farbe haben die Damen- und Herren-Nappalederjacken?

_____

## 15 Beantworte diese Fragen!

1. Was für ein Kleidungsstück möchtest du kaufen?

   _____

2. Was soll das Kleidungsstück kosten?

   _____

3. Welche Farben gefallen dir?

   _____

4. Gibt es in der Nähe, wo du wohnst, ein Kaufhaus?

   _____

5. Was kann man da kaufen?

   _____

6. Wie oft gehst du dorthin?

   _____

7. Wer kommt mit?

   _____

8. Ist es dort preiswert?

   _____

9. Gibt es im Kaufhaus eine große Auswahl.

   _____

## 16 Ergänze die beiden Dialoge!

A: Ich möchte ein Sweatshirt.

B: _____

A: Rot oder blau.

B: _____

A: Es ist zu teuer.

B: _____

A: Wie finden Sie es?

B: _____

A: Ja, Sie haben Recht.

B: _____

A: 15 Euro.

B: _____

*** 

C: Guten Tag!

D: _____

C: Bitte schön?

D: _____

C: Welche Größe?

D: _____

C: Welche Farbe?

D: _____

C: Gefallen Ihnen diese Schuhe?

D: _____

C: Dieses Paar ist etwas preiswerter.

D: _____

C: Ja, sehr gut..

D: _____

C: Gehen Sie bitte zur Kasse!

**17** **Complete each expression by selecting the appropriate verb from the list.**

| | | | | |
|---|---|---|---|---|
| lesen | bleiben | anrufen | fahren | anhaben |
| warten | haben | finden | sein | passen |

1. zu hell _____

2. draußen im Café _____

3. eine große Auswahl _____

4. den Pulli toll _____

5. der Anzug gut _____

6. ein buntes Hemd _____

7. nach Deutschland _____

8. einen Monat in Österreich _____

9. einen Brief _____

10. meine Freunde _____

**18** *Kreuzworträtsel* **(Note: ß = SS)**

**WAAGERECHT**

2. Was ___ sie heute an? Jeans und einen Pulli.

3. Das ist ein kurzes Wort für *Pullover*.

4. Opposite of *kurz*.

7. ___ du, wann er rüberkommt?

8. Das ___ Schuhe steht dir gut.

10. Opposite of *dunkel*.

11. Die Preise sind ___ reduziert.

14. Jana gefällt dunkel ___.

15. Opposite of *draußen*.

**SENKRECHT**

1. Ist es teuer oder ___?

2. Es ist sehr kalt. Du sollst draußen ___ anhaben.

5. Wolf kauft ein Paar ___.

6. Wer die ___ hat, hat die Qual!

9. Welche ___ hat das Hemd? Es ist ganz bunt.

12. Sie bezahlen an der ___.

13. Die Krawatte passt zu diesem ___.

# KAPITEL 8

## Lektion A

**1** **Von wem spricht man hier? Diese Person...**

1. soll einen Radiowecker bekommen. _____

2. hat am Montag Geburtstag. _____

3. kauft Ohrringe. _____

4. sagt, dass Matthias gern Musik hört. _____

5. kommt oft zu spät zur Schule. _____

6. ist sehr klug. _____

7. hat eine Idee für Matthias' Geschenk. _____

8. geht mit Birgit Geschenke kaufen. _____

**2** *Ein besonderer Tag.* **Identify the noun in each sentence. The first letters, when read in sequence, spell the name of a special day. (Note:** *man* **= you, one, they;** *wenn* **= when;** *daraus* **= out of it.)**

1. Zum Geburtstag bekommt man das oft.

   _____

2. Das trinkt man gern mit Eis im Sommer.

   _____

3. Sie will Matthias etwas kaufen.

   _____

4. Man braucht sie, wenn man wissen will, wie spät es ist.

   _____

5. Da kann man die Uhrzeit sehen und auch Musik hören.

   _____

6. Kaffee trinkt man daraus.

   _____

7. Matthias kommt oft zu spät dorthin.

   _____

8. Das braucht man, wenn man anrufen will.

   _____

9. Das ist ein Monat im Sommer.

   _____

10. Birgit meint, Melanie ist das wirklich.

    _____

**3** *Mein Geburtstag.* **Write a short essay *(auf Deutsch)* about your next birthday including the following details: day and month of your birthday, your age, presents you would like to receive and from whom, and what you would like to do on your birthday. Be as creative as possible.**

   _____

   _____

   _____

   _____

   _____

   _____

   _____

   _____

   _____

   _____

   _____

   _____

   _____

   _____

   _____

   _____

**4** Most local newspapers in Germany have announcements for special occasions. Look at some samples and answer the questions. (Note: *feiern* to celebrate; *heiraten* to marry)

Gertrud

**Liebe Oma!**

Ahnungslos schaust Du in die Zeitung rein und denkst bestimmt, das darf nicht sein!

Alles Liebe und Gute zum Geburtstag wünschen Dir

**Deine Kinder und Enkelkinder**

Wir sind überglücklich und freuen uns auf ein Leben mit unserem 2. Enkelsohn

*Justin*

★ 30. 9.

*Als Großeltern*
*Christel und Wolfgang Hübner*

26203 Wardenburg

**50** Allen die an unserem **50**
*Goldenen Hochzeitstag*
so lieb an uns gedacht haben,
sagen wir auf diesem Wege unseren herzlichen Dank.

*Ursula und Werner Antoniewicz*
Oldenburg, Mühlenhofsweg 24

Unsere liebe Mutter, Oma und Uroma
*Berta Martens*

wird heute 80 Jahre.

80 Jahre bist du heut' auf Erden,
das soll nun auch gefeiert werden.
Wir wünschen Dir noch viele Jahre
Gesundheit, Glück und frohe Tage.

**Alles Liebe von**
*Gerda und Peter, Irmi und Georg*
*Mathias, Nicole, Tim, Maike, Sophie & Levin*

# Endlich 18!

**S**üß
**T**reulos
**E**legant
**F**laschenkind
**A**ktiv
**N**aturverbunden

Alles Gute von
Deinen Eltern und 5 Brüdern
Zetel, den 28. 10.

Hurra, hurra, meine Tochter
*Carina Janine*

wird heute 4 Jahr'.

Es gratuliert

**Dein Papa**

Flensburg, den 9. 11.

Heute heiratet
*Torben Bosse seine Mandy*

Ganz besonders freut sich
*Leon-Alexander*
Rantrum, den 3. November

 **Bernd**

Alles Gute zum Geburtstag!

Viel Liebe, Glück und schöne Dinge
in Zukunft jeder Tag Dir bringe!

Es gratuliert zum Geburtstag am 4. November

**Deine Familie**

1. Wer hat am 4. November Geburtstag?

   _____

2. Wie alt ist Berta Martens?

   _____

3. Was feiern Ursula und Werner Antoniewicz?

   _____

4. Wer heiratet heute?

   _____

5. Wer ist jetzt achtzehn Jahre alt?

   _____

6. Wer wünscht seiner Tochter (sie ist vier Jahre alt) herzlichen Glückwunsch
   zum Geburstag?

   _____

7. Wie viele Enkelkinder haben Hübners jetzt?

   _____

8. Wer wünscht Getrud alles Gute zum Geburtstag?

   _____

**5** *Wir gehen zu einer Geburtstagsparty.* **Add the appropriate endings for the definite and indefinite articles and for the possessive adjectives. You will not need endings for all the blanks.**

Am Sonnabend gehen mein_____ Freundin und ich zu einer Party. Gisela

lädt mich und ihr_____ Freunde und Freundinnen zu ihrem Geburtstag ein.

Ihr_____ Mutter kauft ein_____ Kuchen und macht für alle d_____

Abendessen. Ich bringe mein_____ Gitarre mit. D_____ Jugendlichen

werden dann alle singen. Ich gebe Gisela ein _____ Geschenk. Es ist

ein_____ Buch. Ihr_____ Bruder gibt ihr ein_____ Rechner. Jetzt kann

sie d_____ Matheaufgaben schneller machen.

**6** **Complete each sentence using the possessive adjective and noun listed.**

*Beispiel:* Ich besuche (Tante / mein) ___.
Ich besuche meine Tante.

1. Wann kommt (Freundin / dein) _____?

2. Hast du (Fahrrad / sein) _____ gesehen?

3. Ich trage (Jacke / dein) _____ gern.

4. Kennt ihr (Onkel / unser) _____?

5. Was machen (Eltern / euer) _____?

6. Fährst du (Freund / dein) _____ zur Disko?

7. Ohne (Schwester / ihr) _____ gehe ich nicht tanzen.

8. (Auto / mein) _____ ist nicht hier.

9. Kann ich (Mutter / dein) _____ anrufen?

10. Haben Sie (Karte / Ihr) _____, Frau Lehmann?

**7** **Write complete sentences using the words provided. Keep the same word order.**

1. Kennen / Sie / sein / Söhne

   _____

2. Ich / schreiben / mein / Karte

   _____

3. Unser / Kuchen / schmecken / sehr gut

   _____

4. Käthe / kaufen / am Freitag / ihr / Ohrringe

   _____

5. Mein / Geburtstag / sein / am Donnerstag

   _____

6. Frau Müller / müssen / ihr / Tisch / decken

   _____

7. Lesen / ihr / euer / Zeitung / oder / euer / Buch

   _____

8. wann / besuchen / Tina / ihr / Tante

   _____

9. Fahren / unser / Klasse / im Juli / Deutschland

   _____

10. ich / machen / jetzt/ mein / Hausaufgaben / für morgen

   _____

**8** **Rewrite each of the following sentences. First, change each sentence to a question and substitute the proper pronouns for the italicized words.**

*Beispiele:* Ihr kauft *die Karten.*
Kauft ihr sie?

Du hast *seinen Computer.*
Hast du ihn?

1. Du magst *den Film* nicht.

_____

2. Ich soll *meine Lehrerin* holen.

_____

3. Ihr lest *das Buch.*

_____

4. Wir machen *die Arbeit.*

_____

5. Peter besucht *seinen Opa.*

_____

6. Herr Tölz schreibt *die E-Mail.*

_____

7. Du kennst *die Rockmusik* gut.

_____

8. Tina hat *das Geld.*

_____

9. Wir kaufen *einen Fußball.*

_____

10. Sie braucht *ihre Gitarre.*

_____

**9** *Herzlichen Glückwunsch zum Geburtstag!* **The following list represents birthdays of people that fall during the two months as listed.** *Beantworte die Fragen auf Deutsch!*

| GEBURTSTAGSJUBILARE im Juli | |
|---|---|
| 1. Wendlinger, Rudolf | 87 Jhr. |
| 1. Guss, Ursula | |
| 2. Liebhart, Samuel | 70 Jhr. |
| 2. Reinheimer, Max | 50 Jhr. |
| 4. Baumann, Karl | 75 Jhr. |
| 4. Schaly, Edwin | 50 Jhr. |
| 6. Dr. Scharnagl, Anton | 75 Jhr. |
| 6. Dr. Wenzel, Eduard | 70 Jhr. |
| 6. Dr. Porchet, Antoine | 60 Jhr. |
| 6. Schäfer, Gerhard | 55 Jhr. |
| 7. Dr. Holley, Richard | 75 Jhr. |
| 9. Seibold, Ludwig | 55 Jhr. |
| 10. Andres, Heinz | 50 Jhr. |
| 12. Hanauer, Hans | 75 Jhr. |
| 12. Gebert, Franz | 70 Jhr. |
| 12. Lachner, Hans | 60 Jhr. |
| 13. Heinz, Kurt | 60 Jhr. |
| 13. Specht, Helmut | 55 Jhr. |
| 14. Beer, Alfred | 65 Jhr. |
| 14. Vogt, Günter | 50 Jhr. |
| 15. Günther, Karl | 50 Jhr. |
| 15. Käufl, Manfred | 50 Jhr. |
| 15. Moritz, Gilbert | 50 Jhr. |
| 15. Siebert, Günter | 50 Jhr. |
| 16. Friedrich, Hermann | 80 Jhr. |
| 16. Ehrenstrasser, Hans | 55 Jhr. |
| 16. Müller, Ursula | |
| 17. Bald, Albert | 55 Jhr. |
| 18. Schwesinger, Ludwig | 81 Jhr. |
| 19. Reithmeier, Viktor | 60 Jhr. |
| 19. Walter, Georg | 50 Jhr. |
| 20. Gogel, Herbert | 65 Jhr. |
| 20. Schwarzer, Gerhard | 55 Jhr. |
| 21. Schumacher, Helmut | 65 Jhr. |
| 21. Bissinger, Edgar | 55 Jhr. |
| 22. Köppl, Walter | 50 Jhr. |
| 22. Rankl, Franz | 50 Jhr. |
| 23. Maar, Gerhard | 50 Jhr. |
| 24. Spennesberger, Kurt | 65 Jhr. |
| 24. Eich, Josef | 60 Jhr. |
| 24. Stroh, Siegfried | 50 Jhr. |
| 26. Gyoergy, Julia | |
| 27. Antesberger, Hans | 70 Jhr. |
| 28. Dr. Naidenoff, Angel | 70 Jhr. |
| 28. Schmid, Josef | 65 Jhr. |
| 29. Rieder, Walter | 65 Jhr. |
| 29. Waldhauser, Franz | 50 Jhr. |
| 31. Maruhn, Bruno | 70 Jhr. |
| 31. Hasenöhrl, Josef | 65 Jhr. |
| 31. Schrei, Werner | 55 Jhr. |
| 31. Boick, Horst | 50 Jhr. |
| 31. Klausen, Walter | 50 Jhr. |

| GEBURTSTAGSJUBILARE im August | |
|---|---|
| 1. Appel, Harald | 83 Jhr. |
| 1. Pflügler, Franz Karl | 60 Jhr. |
| 1. Klein, Gisela | |
| 2. Lerchenberger, Josef | 80 Jhr. |
| 2. Steinbrunner, H. | 55 Jhr. |
| 2. Sperger, Michael | 50 Jhr. |
| 3. Philipp, Max | 70 Jhr. |
| 3. Giwer, Richard | 65 Jhr. |
| 3. Schoppa, Rainer | 55 Jhr. |
| 4. Poschner, Otto | 82 Jhr. |
| 4. Menzinger, Otto | 70 Jhr. |
| 5. Köppl, Otto | 85 Jhr. |
| 5. Bartu, Manu | 82 Jhr. |
| 5. Giess, Lothar | 50 Jhr. |
| 6. Loy-Birzer, Franz | 60 Jhr. |
| 6. Uhl, Horst | 50 Jhr. |
| 8. Wimmer, Lorenz | 60 Jhr. |
| 9. Dick, Josef | 60 Jhr. |
| 9. Besseling, Josef | 50 Jhr. |
| 10. Zinser, Albert | 83 Jhr. |
| 10. Widmann, Franz | 70 Jhr. |
| 10. Klose, Klaus-Peter | 50 Jhr. |
| 10. Miesl, Willibald | 50 Jhr. |
| 10. Pludra, Jobst-Dieter | 50 Jhr. |
| 11. Bauer, Ludwig | 75 Jhr. |
| 11. Rozsasi, Jvan | 65 Jhr. |
| 11. Meer, Heinz | 55 Jhr. |
| 11. Schmautz, Joachim | 55 Jhr. |
| 12. Dr. Keller, Heinz | 70 Jhr. |
| 12. Sauter, Wilfried | 50 Jhr. |
| 13. Buchschmid, Josef | 75 Jhr. |
| 13. Isko, Willi | 60 Jhr. |
| 13. Moder, Herbert | 55 Jhr. |
| 13. Kohde, Helga | |
| 14. Uhlmann, Erich | 84 Jhr. |
| 14. Schwarzbauer, Walter | 55 Jhr. |
| 15. Biok, Susanne | |
| 15. Lechner, Albert | 70 Jhr. |
| 15. Merk, Josef | 70 Jhr. |
| 15. Nestmann, Therese | |
| 16. Mayer, Adolf | 50 Jhr. |
| 17. Bierstorfer, Anton | 84 Jhr. |
| 17. Becker, Fritz | 50 Jhr. |
| 19. Seidl, Fritz | 70 Jhr. |
| 19. Gensheimer, Ulla | |
| 19. Dasch, Georg | 50 Jhr. |
| 19. Kräutle, Hermann | 50 Jhr. |
| 20. Bachmaier, Sebastian | 55 Jhr. |
| 21. Wollner, Hellmut | 50 Jhr. |
| 24. Riedl, Gert | 50 Jhr. |
| 24. Urban, Rudolf | 50 Jhr. |
| 25. Hofmann, Georg | 50 Jhr. |
| 26. Klein, Ida | |
| 26. Schneider, Michael | 81 Jhr. |
| 27. Bauer, Josef | 75 Jhr. |
| 27. Spiegl, Hans | 70 Jhr. |
| 27. Attenkofer, Rudolf | 50 Jhr. |
| 27. Schmidt, Ernst | 50 Jhr. |
| 28. Schäfer, Max | 75 Jhr. |
| 28. Karrenbauer, Dieter | 50 Jhr. |
| 28. Mosandl, Franz | 50 Jhr. |
| 28. Rienmüller, Alfred | 50 Jhr. |
| 29. Steiner, Reinhard | 55 Jhr. |
| 30. Langreiter, Walter | 50 Jhr. |
| 31. Rocher, Carl | 81 Jhr. |
| 31. Mesow, Helmut | 65 Jhr. |
| 31. Schaper, Karl | 55 Jhr. |

**Das Bayern-Präsidium gratuliert allen Jubilaren recht herzlich!**

1. Wer hat am 21. August Geburtstag?

   _____

2. Wie alt ist Franz Waldhauser?

   _____

3. In welchem Monat hat Gerhard Schäfer Geburtstag?

   _____

4. Wie viele Personen haben am 19. August Geburtstag?

   _____

5. Wie viele Personen heißen Max?

   _____

6. Wissen wir, wie alt Ursula Müller ist?

   _____

7. Wie viele Personen sind im Juli genau 50 Jahre alt?

   _____

8. Wer ist die älteste (oldest) Person? Wie alt ist er?

   _____

# KAPITEL 8

## Lektion B

**10** *In welchem Zimmer findet man das? Im Wohnzimmer, im Schlafzimmer, in der Küche oder im Bad?* **Identify the room in which you would most likely find these items.**

*Beispiel:* der Radiowecker
Im Schlafzimmer.

1. der Herd

_____

2. das Sofa

_____

3. der Schrank

_____

4. die Lampe

_____

5. die Badewanne

_____

6. der Sessel

_____

7. der Geschirrspüler

_____

8. das Spülbecken

_____

9. das Waschbecken

_____

10. der Wecker

_____

Name _____  Datum _____

11 **Was weißt du?** Read the ad and then answer each question using a complete sentence. Here are some words that you may want to know: *die Eckbankgruppe* corner bench group; *sparen* to save

1. Wie viel kostet das komplette Eckregal?

   _____

2. Wie viele Stühle stehen am Tisch?

   _____

3. Was kostet € 519,-?

   _____

4. Wie viel kann man sparen, wenn man das komplette Eckregal kauft?

   _____

5. Wie viel kosten zwei Regale zusammen? Der Eckabschluss und das Eckregal?

_____

6. Wie viele Teile hat die Eckbankgruppe?

_____

## 12 Was passt hier?

_____ 1. Das Wetter soll

_____ 2. Warum machen sie

_____ 3. Sie rufen

_____ 4. Es geht

_____ 5. Oliver, Florian und alle Freunde sind

_____ 6. Olivers Haus ist

_____ 7. Wen wollen Florian und Oliver

_____ 8. Zehn oder zwölf werden

_____ 9. Sie haben

A. nicht ohne Olivers Freunde

B. in Olivers Wohnung keinen Platz

C. ihre Freunde an

D. sehr groß

E. schön sein

F. kommen

G. lieber im Garten

H. die Party nicht da

I. einladen

## 13 Write complete sentences using the words provided.

1. die Jungen / bezahlen / viel / Geld / für / ihr / Fahrräder

_____

2. fahren / Bus / durch / Stadt

_____

3. wir / beginnen / Party / ohne / er

_____

4. die Mädchen / laufen / um / Garten

_____

5. besuchen / ihr / Eiscafé / ohne / euer / Freunde

_____

6. ihr / spielen / morgen / Fußball / gegen / Klasse

_____

7. holen / du / Buch / für / dein / Lehrerin

_____

8. die Jugendlichen / gehen / durch / Bahnhof

_____

**14** *Etwas stimmt hier nicht.* **Rewrite the following incorrect sentences, basing your answers on the** *Lesestück.*

1. Jürgen hat im Herbst Geburtstag.

_____

2. Jürgen hofft, dass er ein Moped bekommt.

_____

3. Er will zwei Jungen und ein Mädchen einladen.

_____

4. Jürgen möchte gern einen Erdbeerkuchen.

_____

5. Jürgen sagt seinen Freunden in der Schule, dass sie kommen sollen.

_____

6. Von Gabi und Silke bekommt Jürgen eine CD.

_____

7. Das große Geschenk ist ein Moped.

_____

8. Jürgen fährt ums Haus.

_____

9. Später sehen die Freunde fern.

_____

10. Frau Sternke bringt das Mittagessen.

_____

## 15 Ergänze die folgenden Dialoge!

A: Kommst du am Mittwoch zu Timos Geburtstag?

B: _____

A: Keine Zeit? Du hast doch sonst nichts zu tun.

B: _____

A: Du hast einen Cousin und eine Cousine?

B: _____

A: Ich kenne Köln gut.

B: _____

A: Meine Großmutter.

B: _____

A: Ein paar Mal im Jahr.

***

C: _____

D: Am Sonnabend besuche ich meine Freundin und am Sonntag gehe ich zum Rockkonzert.

C: _____

D: Um vier.

C: _____

D: Ich weiß noch nicht, vielleicht Stefan und Claudia.

C: _____

D: Prima. Komm doch Viertel vor vier zu mir!

C: _____

D: Eine Karte kostet sechs Euro.

C: _____

D: Tschüs.

## 16  Beende diese Sätze!

1. Das Bücherregal steht _____.

2. In welchem Monat hast du _____?

3. Am Sonnabend möchte ich _____.

4. Ich schenke ihr _____.

5. Herzlichen Glückwunsch _____!

6. Aus der Küche bringt sie _____.

7. Von ihren Schulfreunden bekommt sie _____.

8. Sie will zur Party ihre Freunde _____.

9. Im Juni wird er _____.

10. Was für ein Geschenk _____?

## 17  Complete the following narrative based on the reading selection *Land und Leute (Österreich)*.

Österreich liegt in der Mitte von _____. Dieses Land ist ungefähr

so groß wie der Staat _____. Fast _____ Millionen

Einwohner wohnen in Österreich. Die meisten Österreicher sprechen

_____.

Österreich liegt zum größten Teil in den _____. Der höchste

_____ ist der Großglockner. Die _____ ist der

längste Fluß. Sie fließt von _____ nach Osten.

Die Hauptstadt von Österreich ist _____. Diese Stadt liegt im

_____ Österreichs. Dort ist das Land _____. Viele

Touristen kommen jedes Jahr zum Musikfest nach _____. Die

Stadt Innsbruck ist während jeder _____ beliebt.

## 18  Wie heißen die fünf größten Städte (1-5) Österreichs und wo liegen sie (im Norden, Osten, Süden oder Westen)?

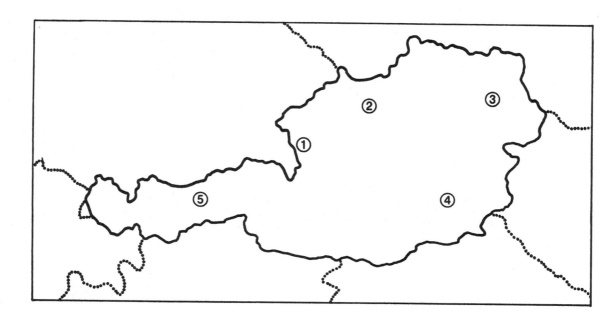

1. _____

2. _____

3. _____

4. _____

5. _____

# 19 Kreuzworträtsel

*Kapitel 8 — Lektion B*

## WAAGERECHT

3. Oliver und Florian ___ ihre Freunde an. Sie wollen wissen, wer zur Party kommt.

4. Das sind Ohrringe.

7. Er ___ auf einem Sofa.

8. Es steht im Schlafzimmer.

9. Das hat Jürgen. Er wird sechzehn.

13. Da kann man Musik und Nachrichten hören.

15. Von Gabi und Silke bekommt Jürgen einen ___.

17. Jürgen will Christian, Silke und Gabi zum Geburtstag ___.

18. Da kann man die Sportschau und Nachrichten sehen.

19. Jürgen ___ am nächsten Tag seinen Schulfreunden den Motorroller.

## SENKRECHT

1. Birgit sagt Melanie, dass sie wirklich ein ___ ist.

2. Jürgen ___ gern Schwarzwälder Kirschtorte.

5. Das bekommt Jürgen von seinem Vater.

6. Melanie ___ für ihre Mutter Ohrringe.

9. Jürgen fährt auf seinem Motorroller ohne Helm durch den ___.

10. Sie ist im Badezimmer.

11. Jürgen hat im ___ Geburtstag.

12. In Olivers Wohnung ___ sie keinen Platz für die Party.

14. Frau Sternke macht am Abend eine Kalte ___.

16. Jürgen ___ ein paar Geschenke auf.

# KAPITEL 9

## Lektion A

**1 Was passt hier?**

_____ 1. Was gibt's                    A. heute Nachmittag nichts vor

_____ 2. Karin muss                    B. vor

_____ 3. Gülten hat                    C. sie nicht an

_____ 4. Kommt Sarah                   D. einkaufen

_____ 5. Im Kino läuft                 E. bestimmt Tobias mit

_____ 6. Wann fängt                    F. im Kino

_____ 7. Sarah bringt                  G. der Film an

_____ 8. Was hast du                   H. toll sein

_____ 9. Der Film soll                 I. ein Horrorfilm

_____10. Warum rufst du                J. zu Karin rüber

**2 Was läuft in den Kinos?** Look at the movie schedule and then answer the questions.

**Nienburg, Film-Eck, Kino 1:** „Thomas, die rote Lokomotive", Sa. 15 Uhr, So. 16 Uhr; „Space Cowboys", Sa. 17, 20, 22.45 Uhr, So. 18, 20 Uhr; **Kino 2:** „Der kleine Vampir", Sa. 15 Uhr, So. 16 Uhr; „Es begann im September", Sa. 17 Uhr, So. 18 Uhr; „Wonderboys", täglich 20 Uhr; „Sekunden der Entscheidung", Sa. 22.45 Uhr; **Kino 3:** „Der Weg nach El Dorado", Sa. 15 Uhr, So. 16 Uhr; „Shang-High Noon", Sa. 17, 22.45 Uhr, So. 18 Uhr; **Shaft – Noch Fragen?**", täglich 20 Uhr.

**Hoya, Filmhof:** „Der Weg nach El Dorado", täglich 15 Uhr; „Space Cowboys", Sa. 20, 22.30 Uhr, So. 20 Uhr; „Der Krieger und die Kaiserin", täglich 20 Uhr; „Scary Movie", Sa. 22.30 Uhr, So. 19 Uhr; „Ich, Beide & Sie", täglich 15, 17 Uhr; „Grasgeflüster", täglich 17 Uhr; „Zurück zu Dir", So. 11 Uhr

**Syke, Hansa-Kino:** „Pokémon", täglich 15 Uhr; „Thomas, die fantastische Lokomotive", täglich 15 Uhr; „Ich, Beide & Sie", Sa. 17, 22.30 Uhr, So. 17 Uhr; „Space Cowboys", Sa. 20, 22.30 Uhr, So. 17, 20 Uhr; „Es begann im September", täglich 20 Uhr; **Film-Plakat-Frühschoppen:** 11 bis 14 Uhr

**Sulingen, Filmpalast:** „Ich, Beide & Sie", täglich 15 Uhr; „Familie Klumps und der verrückte Professor", täglich 15 Uhr; „Scary Movie", Sa. 19 Uhr, So. 17.30 Uhr; „Es begann im September", Sa. 20.45 Uhr, So. 20 Uhr; „Space Cowboys", Sa. 20.15, 23 Uhr, So. 17, 20.15 Uhr; „Shang-High Noon", Sa. 23 Uhr

1. In wie vielen Kinos läuft der Film *Es begann im September?*

   _____

2. Um wie viel Uhr beginnt der Film *Ich, Beide & Sie* im Filmpalast?

   _____

3. In welcher Stadt ist das *Film-Eck?*

   _____

4. An welchen zwei Tagen läuft der Film *Space Cowboys* im Filmhof?

   _____

5. Um wie viel Uhr beginnt der Film *Grasgeflüster?*

   _____

6. In welchem Kino läuft der Film *Familie Klumps und der verrückte Professor?*

   _____

7. Welcher Film beginnt am frühesten *(the earliest)* am Sonntag?

   _____

8. Welcher Film läuft am spätesten *(the latest)* und nur einmal *(once)* am Tag? An welchem Tag?

   _____

**3** ***Was die Leute gern in Lichtenfels machen!*** **The following are examples of leisure-time activities that take place in Lichtenfels, located in southern Germany. Look at the ads and tell if the description fits one of these four activities:** *Bootsverleih* **boat rental;** *Minigolf, Tennis* **or** *Wandern* **hiking. Some additional words to know are:** *die Brücke* **bridge;** *geöffnet* **open;** *markiert* **marked.**

## **B**ootsverleih

Stadtteil Schney
Telefon: 09571 / 3814 oder 2298
***Öffnungszeiten:***
Täglich ab 8.00 Uhr bis abends;
für Gruppen Voranmeldung
erbeten
***Benutzungspreise:***

| | | | |
|---|---|---|---|
| Einerkajaks | € 4,– | | |
| Kahn | € 4,50 | bis € 6,– | pro Stunde |
| Paddelboot | € 4,– | pro Stunde | |
| Canadier | € 4,50 | und € 6,– | pro Stunde |
| Tretboot | € 6,– | pro Stunde | |

*Fahrtstrecke:* Auf dem Main (4 km)
Die Boote werden auch für Halbtages-, Tages- oder Mehrtagestouren
verliehen.

➙ Marktplatz - Coburger Straße - Mainbrücke - Stadt verlassen - erste
Straße rechts nach Schney - erste Straße rechts zur Mainlust

### **SEICA-Bootsvermietung**

Canadier- und Erlebnisreisen  Telefon 09571 / 7 33 91
Selbstfahrer oder geführte Bootsfahrten mit Programm. Rückholung der
Boote. Tourenstrecken auf dem Main von 7km, 14km und 20km.

## **M**inigolf

***Minigolfanlage
mit Pit-Pat und Boccia***
Alte Coburger Straße 40,
Telefon 09571 / 3904

***Öffnungszeiten:***
April - September
werktags    13.00 - 22.00 Uhr
Sa/So       10.00 - 22.00 Uhr
Oktober Wochenendbetrieb

*Eintrittspreise*
Erwachsene und Kinder € 1,50

➙ Marktplatz - Coburger Straße - nach der Mainbrücke 2. Straße links -
Berg hochfahren

## **T**ennis

***im Sportpark
an der Friedenslinde,***
Telefon 09571 / 70623
Drei-Feld-Tennishalle mit
Ballwurfmaschine und
Video-Anlage,
zusätzlich 3 Freiplätze.
Trainerstunden nach Vereinb.

***Öffnungszeiten:***
Sommer täglich von      10.00 - 24.00Uhr
Winter täglich von       9.00 - 24.00 Uhr
*Sauna, Solarium, Restaurant.*

➙ Marktplatz - Oberes Tor- Kronacher Straße bis Polizei - danach
rechts den Berg hoch (Rennleinsweg) - nach der Brücke auf der
linken Seite

### ***Tennisclub Lichtenfels***

Tennisgelände am Main,
8 Freiplätze,
Trainerstunden nach Vereinbarung
mit H. Rohrbacher, Telefon 09571/798195

➙ Marktplatz - Coburger Straße - vor der Mainbrücke links

## **W**andern

■ ***Geführte Wanderungen
mitgeselliger Einkehr***
Anmeldung im Verkehrsamt
■ Markierte Wanderwege:
– Fritsch Wanderkarte
Oberes Maintal, Coburg,
Lichtenfels, Staffelstein
1 : 50.000 – oder Fritsch
Umgebungskarte
Lichtenfels, Staffelstein
1 : 35.000

1.  Man kann diesen Sport (mit Netzen) gleich nach der Brücke spielen.

   _____

2.  Es ist vom April bis September geöffnet.

   _____

3. Das macht man in Coburg, Lichtenfels und Staffelstein.

   _____

4. Da kann man auf dem Main vier Kilometer fahren.

   _____

5. Man kann mit H. Rohrbacher trainieren.

   _____

6. Es ist im Winter jeden Tag fünfzehn Stunden geöffnet.

   _____

7. Eine Karte kostet € 1,50.

   _____

8. Ein Paddelboot kostet € 4,- pro Stunde.

   _____

## 4 Fill in the correct prefixes.

1. Hast du heute etwas _____?

2. Karin macht ihre Geschenke _____.

3. Ich lade meine Freunde zum Geburtstag _____.

4. Rolf hat heute seinen neuen Pulli _____.

5. Kommst du ins Kino _____?

6. Um wie viel Uhr beginnt das Fernsehprogramm? Um acht, dann sehen wir

   _____.

7. Warum kommst du nicht später zu mir _____?

8. Wir haben keine Zeit. Deshalb gehen wir gleich _____.

**5** *Was machen Klaus und Gabi?* **Klaus and Gabi are involved in various activities as indicated in the illustration. In paragraph form, write 10 sentences (5 for Klaus and 5 for Gabi) that describe what they are doing. Be as creative as possible!**

# Klaus

_____

_____

_____

_____

_____

_____

_____

_____

_____

_____

# Gabi

_____

_____

_____

_____

_____

_____

_____

_____

_____

**6** *Im Theater.* **Read the ad announcing various theater performances that are taking place. Answer the questions that follow. (Note:** *stattfinden* **to take place)**

## SPIELPLAN 4.11. bis 12.11.

**OPERNHAUS**

| | | |
|---|---|---|
| SA. 04.11. | 20.00 | **DIE SCHÖPFUNG** Abo B, ThG blau*/Preise B |
| SO. 05.11. | Ab 10.00 | **BRUNCH IM FOYER** |
| | 11.00 | **JAZZFRÜHSCHOPPEN** |
| | 16.00–21.40 | **GÖTTERDÄMMERUNG** (Wiederaufnahme) Abo NA*/ Preise A |
| | Anschließend | **NACHGEHAKT** (Oberes Foyer) |
| Mi. 08.11. | 11.00–13.00 | **PAPAGENO SPIELT AUF DER ZAUBERFLÖTE*** |
| DO. 09.11. | 20.00–22.45 | **EIN MASKENBALL** ThG 5831–6360, 6891–7420, ThG rot*/Preise C, Unikat ab PG III |
| FR. 10.11. | 19.30–22.45 | **DIE ZAUBERFLÖTE** (Wiederaufnahme) ThG 4771–5300, 7951–8480*/Preise B, Unikat ab PG III |
| SA. 11.11. | 15.00–17.00 | **CAFÉ CONCERT** (Oberes Foyer) |
| | 20.00–22.45 | **TURANDOT***/Preise B |
| SO. 12.11. | Ab 10.00 | **BRUNCH IM FOYER** |
| | 11.00 | **KAMMERMUSIKALISCHE MATINÉE: WALZER IM QUADRAT** (Schauspielhaus)*/ |
| | 18.30 | **KURZEINFÜHRUNG** (Oberes Foyer) |
| | 19.00 | **COMBATTIMENTO DI TANCREDI E CLORINDA/HERZOG BLAUBARTS BURG** Abo G*/Preise B |
| | Anschließend | **NACHGEHAKT** (Oberes Foyer) |

**SCHAUSPIELHAUS**

| | | |
|---|---|---|
| SA. 04.11. | 19.30 | **DIE VERSCHWÖRUNG DES FIESCO ZU GENUA***/Preise E |
| SO. 05.11. | 20.00 | **DAS BLUT** (DE) Abo W2*/Preise E |
| MO. 06.11. | 19.00 | **KURZEINFÜHRUNG** (Foyer) |
| | 19.30 | **DIE VERSCHWÖRUNG DES FIESCO ZU GENUA***/Preise F |
| DI. 07.11. | 18.00 | Geschlossene Veranstaltung der Deutschen Bank |
| FR. 10.11 | 20.00 | **LEONCE UND LENA** ThG 6361–6890*/Preise E |
| SA. 11.11. | 20.00 | **SEKAI** (Premiere)*/Preise C |
| SO. 12.11. | 20.00 | **SEKAI***/Preise E |

**WERKHAUS**

| | | |
|---|---|---|
| MI. 08.11. | 19.30 | **KURZEINFÜHRUNG** (Studio) |
| | 20.00 | **PHAIDRAS LIEBE** (Studio)* |
| | Anschließend | **NACHGEHAKT** (Studio) |
| FR. 10.11. | 20.00 | **APROPOS „FIESCO"** hypersound concrète (Studio)* |
| SO. 12.11. | 20.00 | **PHAIDRAS LIEBE** (Studio)* |

**SCHNAWWL**

| | | |
|---|---|---|
| DI. 07.11. | 19.00 | **PÄDAGOGEN-JOUR-FIXE** |
| MI. 08.11. | 19.00–21.10 | Öffenliche Hauptprobe für Pädagoginnen: **DER METEORITENLÖFFEL** Bitte anmelden! |
| SA. 11.11. | 19.00–21.10 | **DER METEORITENLÖFFEL** (Premiere)* |

*= Freier Verkauf - Änderungen vorbehalten!*
**Kartentelefon: Di. bis Fr. 9.00–17.00 Uhr, Mo. und Sa. 9.00–13.00 Uhr**
Nationaltheater • Tel. (06 21) 16 80-150; Fax (06 21) 16 80 - 258
Schnawwl • Tel. (06 21) 16 80 - 302

101549489_6917270

Name _____ Datum _____

1. In welcher Stadt ist das Nationaltheater?

   _____

2. An welchem Tag und um wie viel Uhr findet *Götterdämmerung* statt?

   _____

3. In welchem Theater kann man *Die Verschwörung des Fiesco zu Genua* sehen?

   _____

4. Von welchem Monat ist dieser Spielplan?

   _____

5. Um wie viel Uhr und wo am Sonntag im November kann man Jazz hören?

   _____

6. Was kann man am Mittwoch um 20.00 Uhr im Werkhaus sehen?

   _____

7. Wie ist die Telefonnummer vom Nationaltheater?

   _____

8. An welchem Tag kann man keine Karten am Telefon bekommen?

   _____

**7** *Musikantenfestival.* **Austria is known for its many musical performances. Virtually every town has several musical events throughout the year. Review the following announcement and then choose the most appropriate ending for each beginning.**

_____ 1. Die Almfestwoche beginnt

_____ 2. Die jungen Original Oberkrainer singen

_____ 3. Gregors Vater heißt auch

_____ 4. Die Stoakogler kommen

_____ 5. Die Jetzendorfer Hinterhof-musikanten sind

_____ 6. Nach den Stoakoglern kommen

_____ 7. Der 5. Juli ist

_____ 8. Die Mitterling Buam kommen

A. aus der Steiermark

B. ein Donnerstag

C. die Mitterling Buam

D. aus Großarl

E. Slavko (Avsenik)

F. eine Stimmungs- und Showkapelle

G. am 23. Juni

H. am 6. Juli

**8** **Find the matching words from the following list to form compound nouns. Include the article as well. Then write sentences using the compound nouns.**

> das Land   der Ball   der Saft   die Sahne   der Tag
> das Geschäft   die Wanne   der Hof   die Tasche   das Essen

1. der Apfel: _____

   _____

2. die Bahn: _____

   _____

3. die Geburt: _____

   _____

4. das Bad: _____

   _____

5. der Fuß: _____

   _____

6. die Musik: _____

   _____

7. der Mittag: _____

   _____

8. der Nachbar: _____

   _____

9. der Schlag: _____

   _____

10. die Schule: _____

   _____

# KAPITEL 9

## Lektion B

**9** *Was macht Karsten alles an diesem Tag?* **Karsten has a busy day. Describe everything that he is doing, according to the illustrations. Follow the descriptive sequence as indicated by numbers.**

_____

_____

_____

_____

_____

_____

_____

_____

_____

_____

_____

**10** *Im Kino.* **Imagine that you and your friends have just arrived at a movie theater. Complete the following two dialogs. In the first dialog, you go to the ticket counter and ask the clerk a few questions. In the second dialog you talk to your friend.**

| | |
|---|---|
| *Du:* | _____ |
| *Angestellte:* | Heute läuft der Film „Betty und ihre Schwestern". |
| *Du:* | _____ |
| *Angestellte:* | Ja, er soll ganz toll sein. |
| *Du:* | _____ |
| Angestellte: | Der nächste Film beginnt um sieben Uhr. |
| *Du:* | _____ |
| *Angestellte:* | Eine Karte kostet sechs Euro. |
| *Du:* | _____ |
| *Angestellte:* | Da drüben. |

*Du:* _____

*Freundin:* Ich habe nur fünf Euro.

*Du:* _____

*Freundin:* Kannst du mir zwei Euro geben?

*Du:* _____

*Freundin:* Bis morgen, dann bekommst du es wieder.

*Du:* _____

*Freundin:* Ich möchte Popcorn und eine Cola kaufen.

*Du:* _____

*Freundin:* Danke.

## 11 Change each of the sentences into command forms.

1. Du kommst um sieben zur Party.

   _____

2. Ihr macht die Arbeit.

   _____

3. Sie schreiben eine E-Mail, Frau Arndt.

   _____

4. Wir kaufen Klaus einen Fußball.

   _____

5. Ihr hört die Musik im Radio.

   _____

6. Sie lesen das Buch bis morgen.

   _____

7. Du bringst eine Gitarre mit.

   _____

8. Wir bleiben etwas länger.

   _____

**12** *Die Pastell Rockband.* **In the** *Lesestück* **of this chapter you have become familiar with Mona, who is a member of the** *Pastell* **rock band. Read what she is saying about herself in the following authentic text and then answer the questions.**

## Hallo, ich bin Mona.

Seit sieben Jahren singe ich bei Pastell. Das ist eine lange Zeit. Wir haben ganz von vorne angefangen, die meisten in der Gruppe konnten noch kein Instrument spielen, als wir anfingen. Ich selbst hatte drei Jahre lang Cello-Unterricht, fand aber das Singen viel interessanter. Gut bei der klassischen Ausbildung war, das ich Musiktheorie mit Praxis verbinden konnte und mein Gehör geschult wurde.

Pastell befinden sich gerade in einer Umbauphase. Wir verraten noch nicht, wer in Zukunft bei Pastell mitmachen wird.

Unsere Band-Geschichte war ganz schön aufregend. Wir haben zwei CDs produziert, jede Menge Lieder geschrieben und sehr viele Konzerte gegeben. Höhepunkte waren u. a. die Auslandstournéen nach Luxemburg, Frankreich, Irland, England, Dänemark und zur Insel Réunion im Indischen Ozean, wo wir zwei Mal unterwegs waren und sehr viele Freunde gefunden haben.

In den sieben Jahren haben wir mehrfach die Musiker ausgewechselt. Das ist eigentlich normal, denn als Schüler mit ca. 13-18 Jahren weiß man noch nicht so genau, was man will oder kann... Das Rockprojekt gibt vielen Musikern eine Chance. Zum Glück bietet es auch immer neue Kontakte.

1. How many years has Mona been part of *Pastell?*

   _____

2. How experienced was the group when they started?

   _____

3. What instrument did Mona play and for how long?

   _____

4. What did she prefer rather than playing an instrument?

   _____

5. Does she reveal who will be part of the rebuilt *Pastell* group?

_____

6. How many CDs did the band produce?

_____

7. What else did the band do besides producing CDs?

_____

8. How many times was the band in the area of the Indian Ocean?

_____

9. What don't students at the age of 13 to 18 know?

_____

10. What does her own and her band members' involvement as a group offer?

_____

## 13 *Was fehlt hier?* Provide the missing details based on the *Lesestück*.

1. Pastell ist eine deutsche _____.

2. Nicht alle Mitglieder kommen aus _____.

3. Die Rockgruppe gibt in Frankreich und England _____.

4. Ihre beliebte CD heißt „Alle _____ dieser Welt."

5. Man kann sie manchmal im _____ sehen.

6. Mona ist _____ in dieser Gruppe.

7. In der Band spielt Mona Cello und _____.

8. Ugur hat _____ gern.

9. Daniel kommt aus _____.

10. Alinas _____ macht keine Musik in der Band.

11. Dennis spielt _____ in der Band.

**14** *Eine bekannte Rockband in den sechziger Jahren.* **Fill in the correct words. The first letters, when read in sequence, spell the name of a famous rock band from three to four decades ago. Write each word or name in capital letters.**

1. Wir gehen nicht ins Kino. Wir gehen lieber in eine _____.

   Dort können wir tanzen.

2. Alinas Hobbys sind Schlagzeug, _____, Reisen und Kosmetik.

3. England und Frankreich liegen in _____.

4. Sammelst du gern _____? Ja, ich bekomme viele Briefe aus

   anderen Ländern.

5. Wo gehst du _____? Im Kaufhaus.

6. Was gibst du für die Karten _____? Nur zwanzig Euro.

7. Ugur ist kein Deutscher. Er ist _____.

8. Wie lange wird der Film denn _____? Mehr als zwei Stunden.

9. Dennis _____ ist Gitarrist bei Pastell.

10. Mona ist _____. Sie singt sehr gern.

**15** *Wo und was?* Match the locations with the various activities that take place there.

Ⓐ Hamburg-Marathon    16.4.
Hamburg
Messe (Start und Ziel)
Mit internationaler Betei-
ligung
Kontakt: 040/616773
•••

Ⓑ Radrennen rund um    1.5.
den Henninger Turm
Frankfurt, Hessen, Start
am Henninger Turm
Deutscher Radklassiker
Nr. 1, mit Topteams aus
aller Welt
Kontakt: 06196/508631
•••

Ⓒ Kulturfestival Ulmer Zelt    24.5.-8.7.
Ulm, Baden-Württemberg
Friedrichsau
Varieté, Rock, Pop, Jazz,
Blues und Kinderpro-
gramm, namhafte inter-
nationale Künstler
Kontakt: 0731/9608513
•••

Ⓓ Filmfest    24.6.-1.7.
München, Bayern
In verschiedenen Kinos
Internationale Filmszene
mit Welturaufführungen
Kontakt: 089/3819040
•••

Ⓔ Rock im Park    9.-11.6.
Nürnberg, Bayern
Frankenstadion und
Umfeld
Europas größtes
Rockfestival mit rund
100 Bands
Kontakt: 0911/ 4719301
•••

Ⓕ Kieler Woche    17.-25.6.
Kiel, Schleswig-Holstein
Hafen
Das Wimbledon des
Segelns
Kontakt: 0431/9012402
•••

Ⓖ Jazzfest Gronau    24.-30.4.
Gronau,
Nordrhein-Westfalen
An verschiedenen Orten
Größtes internationales
Jazz-Festival in Nord-
rhein-Westfalen
Kontakt: 02562/120
•••

Ⓗ 69. Mozartfest    31.5.-2.7.
Würzburg, Bayern
An verschiedenen Orten
Berühmte Solisten und
Orchester
Kontakt: 0931/373336
•••

_____ 1. München
_____ 2. Gronau
_____ 3. Hamburg
_____ 4. Ulm
_____ 5. Würzburg
_____ 6. Kiel
_____ 7. Frankfurt
_____ 8. Nürnberg

A. Many long-distance runners will come here to compete.

B. Bicyclists from all over the world will compete in a race.

C. International artists will perform various types of music and appear in a children's program.

D. Various international films are shown here.

E. This city will host Europe's largest rock festival.

F. Many sailors will come here to this harbor city and compete.

G. The largest international jazz festival takes places in this town and several other towns or cities in this area.

H. Famous soloists and orchestras will perform in this city and its surroundings.

**16** **Complete each expression by selecting the most appropriate verb from the following list. Use each verb only once.**

| laufen | fotografieren | aufräumen | singen | einkaufen | gehen |
| mitbringen | decken | sammeln | machen | lesen | vorschlagen |

1. das Zimmer _____

2. Briefmarken _____

3. den Tisch _____

4. einen Freund _____

5. ein Lied _____

6. im Kaufhaus _____

7. Krafttraining _____

8. Familienmitglieder beim Geburtstag _____

9. Ski _____

10. eine Zeitung _____

11. ins Kino _____

12. eine Reise _____

Datum

17 **Kreuzworträtsel**

## WAAGERECHT

1. Ein anderes Wort für „beginnen".

3. Die CD heißt „Alle Farben dieser ___."

8. Ich muss noch das ___ spülen.

9. Was sammelst du? ___.

11. Was singt ihr? Deutsche ___.

12. Das ist ein Telefon.

14. Alina ___ aus Finnland.

16. ___ nicht immer so viel Geld aus!

18. Musst du heute Nachmittag den ___ mähen?

## SENKRECHT

2. ___ du gern? Nein, ich habe keine Kamera.

4. Sarah ___ noch ihr Zimmer aufräumen.

5. Frau Weber kauft Gemüse auf dem ___.

6. Warum haben alle so viel Spaß? Er macht immer tolle ___.

7. Daniels ___ ist Michael Schumacher.

10. Immer mit der ___!

13. Kannst du den Tisch bitte ___?

14. Dort laufen oft neue Filme.

15. ___ kommt aus Wuppertal und singt bei Pastell.

17. Ugur spielt ___.

# KAPITEL 10

## Lektion A

**1** **Was passt hier?**

_____ 1. Das stimmt. Du hast wieder

_____ 2. Er ist nicht mehr neu. Von wem
ist denn dieser

_____ 3. Ich treibe keine

_____ 4. Im Winter laufen sie gern

_____ 5. Zum Geburtstag bekommt er
viele

_____ 6. Wir sprechen über das

_____ 7. Was wünschst du dir zum

_____ 8. Robert bekommt tolle Sachen
von seinen

A. Geschenke

B. Geburtstag

C. Sportart

D. Eltern

E. Fußball

F Schlittschuh

G. Abitur

H. Recht

**2** You will find seven different kinds of sports in the word find. The letters may go backward or forward; they may go up, down, across or diagonally. However, they go only one way in any one word. (ß = SS)

```
S  I  N  N  E  T  H  C  S  I  T
L  M  E  Z  I  A  N  U  F  L  B
L  Q  F  U  S  S  B  A  L  L  E
A  Z  A  W  H  G  O  N  S  A  F
B  T  W  U  O  X  N  I  P  B  E
Y  A  B  L  C  N  N  B  O  T  S
E  N  F  Z  K  N  F  K  N  E  R
L  S  N  A  E  R  C  M  V  K  W
L  L  R  T  Y  H  J  Z  B  S  O
O  R  Q  W  F  E  O  I  P  A  X
V  O  E  M  D  W  K  X  A  B  C
```

## 3 Was *machen alle?* Look at the six different activities and then write a sentence that describes what everyone is doing.

1. _____

2. _____

3. _____

4. _____

5. _____

6. _____

**4** **Fill in the proper form of the article and noun for those given in parentheses.**

1. Ich gebe (dein Onkel) _____ eine Landkarte.

2. Kauf (das Mädchen) _____ eine CD!

3. Kannst du (unser Opa) _____ eine Karte schicken?

4. Wir sollen (die Lehrerin) _____ die Arbeit geben.

5. Schicken Sie (mein Vater) _____ eine E-Mail!

6. Wir kaufen (die Tante) _____ ein Geschenk.

7. Hol (ihr Bruder) _____ die Skier!

8. Warum gibst du (deine Freundin) _____ so ein großes Geschenk?

**5** *Tennis in Essen.* **The city of Essen offers many indoor and outdoor tennis facilities. Look at the chart and answer the questions. Some words that you may need to know are:** *Zahl der Freiplätze* **number of outdoor courts;** *Zahl der Hallenplätze* **number of indoor courts;** *Öffnungszeiten* **business hours;** *ganzjährig* **all year round;** *Kursus* **course;** *geöffnet* **open.**

**Tennissport**

| Ort | Ortsteil Straße | Zahl der Freiplätze | Zahl der Hallen-plätze | Öffnungszeiten | Kosten pro Person und Stunde a) Tennis spielen b) Trainerstunde | Anschrift des Clubs bzw. Vermieters |
|---|---|---|---|---|---|---|
| **Essen** | Bergeborbeck Hafenstr. 10 | 12 | 12 | Sommer 9.00–22.00 Winter 7.00–23.00 | a) 7,–/8,– (Sommer) 14,– (Winter) b) 160,– (Kursus, 12 Std.) | Essener Tennishallengemeinschaft Hafenstr. 10 4300 Essen, Tel. (0201) 66 15 80 |
| | Altenessen Hesslerstr. 37 | – | 4 | ganzjährig 7.00–24.00 | a) 5,–/8,– (Sommer) 8,–/13,– (Winter) b) 18,– | Altenessener Tennishallen Altenessen, Hesslerstr. 37 4300 Essen, Tel. (0201) 34 72 72 |
| | Kray Rotthauser Str. 46 | 5 | 3 | ganzjährig 8.00–22.00 | a) 8,–/14,– | Tennishallen Essen-Kray Rotthauser Str. 46 4300 Essen, Tel. (0201) 5 59 55 |
| | Süd Schürmannstraße | 8 | 12 | ganzjährig 7.00–23.00 | a) 11,–/12,– (Sommer) 15,–/16,– (Winter) b) 30,– (45 Min.) | Tennis- und Squash-Park Schürmannstraße 19a, 4300 Essen Tel. (0201) 25 58 71 |
| | Kettwig, Oberlehberg 60 | 3 | 7 | 7.00–23.00 (Halle ganzjährig 7.00–21.00 (Freiplatz) | a) 9,–/12,– (Halle Sommer) 11,–/16,– (Halle Winter) 5,– (Freiplatz) | Tennishalle Kettwig Oberlehberg 60, 4300 Essen Tel. (02054) 1 66 88 |
| | Adlerstraße | 2 | 4 | ganzjährig 8.00–23.00 | a) 10,– b) 23,–/25,– | Tennis-Center Adlerstr. 14, 4300 Essen Tel. (0201) 55 26 26 |
| | Worringstraße | 5 | – | 7.00–23.00 | a) 9,–/14,– | Tennishalle Geneal Worringstr. 250, 4300 Essen Tel. (0201) 5 77 75 |
| | Schroertal | – | 4 | ganzjährig 7.00–24.00 | a) 10,–/13,– b) 24,– | Tenniscollege Schroertal 32, 4300 Essen Tel. (0201) 48 19 91 |
| | Grugapark | 4 | – | Sommer 8.00–21.00 Winter 9.00–16.30 | a) 6,– + Eintritt (Sommerabonne-ment 80,–) | Grugapark Külshammer Weg 32, 4300 Essen Tel. (0201) 88 – 78 07 |
| | Am Zehnthof | – | 10 | Sommer 15.00–23.00 Winter 7.00–23.00 | a) 12,– (Sommer) 13,–/16,– (Winter) | Tennis-Treff Am Zehnthof 4300 Essen, Tel. (0201) 59 72 73 ab 15.00 Uhr |

1. Wie viel kostet es, wenn man im Tennis-Center (Adlerstraße) spielen will?

_____

2. Wie viele Freiplätze gibt es im Grugapark?

_____

3. Wie teuer ist ein Kursus für 12 Stunden bei der Essener Tennishallen-gemeinschaft?

_____

4. Wie viele Tennisplätze (Frei- und Hallenplätze) gibt es im Tennis- und Squash- Park (Schürmannstraße)?

_____

5. Wie ist die Telefonnummer für das Tennis-Treff Am Zehnthof?

_____

6. Was sind die Öffnungszeiten in den Tennishallen Essen-Kray?

_____

7. Wie viele Stunden sind die Altenessener Tennishallen geöffnet?

_____

**6** *Wintersport in Willingen.* **The area around Willingen offers a variety of winter sports activities. Look at the description and answer the questions. Some words that you may need to know are:** *die Autobahn* **freeway;** *östlich* **east of;** *der Skiverleih* **ski rentals;** *die Vorwahl wählen* **to dial area code;** *die Postleitzahl* **zip code.**

### Skiliftgesellschaften

| | | |
|---|---|---|
| Seilbahnverwaltungs GmbH & Co | Tel.: | 67 15 |
| Ettelsberg-Seilschwebebahn KG | Fax: | 96 82 01 |
| Zur Hoppeke 5, 34508 Willingen | | |
| Wildparklifte Hans Schlömer | Tel.: | 62 32 |
| Am Ettelsberg 1, 34508 Willingen | Fax.: | 6 90 66 |
| Skiliftgemeinschaft Köhlerhagen | Tel.: | 6 94 48 |
| Am Köhlerhagen, 34508 Willingen | Tel.: | 66 21 |
| Gebr. Rummel GmbH & Co KG | Tel.: | 96 69 77 |
| Sonnenlift und Ritzhagenlifte | Fax: | 96 69 78 |
| Am Hoppern, 34508 Willingen | | |

*Vorwahl aus dem Ausland 00 49-56 32

### Skiverleih und Servicestationen

| | | |
|---|---|---|
| Skiverleih der Skischule Willingen | Tel.: | 64 54 |
| Service und Skidepot | | 66 16 |
| Am Ritzhagen | | |
| Skiverleih WiWa | Tel.: | 6 99 39 |
| Direkt am Skilift Ritzhagen | Mobil: | 0172/2 33 80 47 |
| Skiverleih Sporthaus Kesper | Tel.: | 63 50 |
| Carving, Snowboard, Langlauf, Rodel | Fax: | 6 92 49 |
| Gegenüber der Talstation Sesselbahn | | |
| Neuhaus Ski-Verleih-Verhuur | Tel.: | 96 80 90 |
| Carving, Big Food, Snowboard, Langlauf | Tel.: | 41 91 |
| Gegenüber Sesselbahn | Fax: | 96 80 91 |
| Skiverleih Udo Nackas | Tel.: | 92 70 80 |
| Am Wild- und Freizeitpark | | |
| Skiverleih und Werkstatt Wilh. Wilke | Tel.: | 61 78 |
| Talstation Sonnenlift | | |
| Sport-Scholz | Tel.: | 64 43 |
| Skiverleih/Skiservice | Fax: | 6 90 51 |
| Carving, Snowboard, Langlauf | | |
| Langlauf-Skischule + Langlauf-Skiverleih, | Tel.: | 65 80 |
| Dieter Stremme, Am Dicken Stein 6a, | Fax: | 6 98 49 |
| Sammelplatz am Skiverleih Café Paradies | | |

### Die Willinger Skischulen
Vorwahl* 0 56 32

| | | |
|---|---|---|
| Skischule Willingen | Tel.: | 64 54 |
| Alpin, Snowboard, Langlauf | | 66 16 |
| Sammelplatz Skiverleih Ritzhagen | | |
| DSV-Skischule Upland in Willingen | Tel.: | 9 64 88 |
| Alpin+Snowboard | | 70 21 |
| Sammelplatz an der Sesselbahn | | |
| Anmeldung Skiverleih Neuhaus | | |
| DSV-Skischule Hessen WiWa | Tel.: | 6 99 39 |
| Sammelplatz Skilift Ritzhagen | Mobil: | 0172/2 33 80 47 |
| Skischule Hochsauerland, Udo Nackas | Tel.: | 92 70 80 |
| Wildparklifte | | |

1. Zwischen welchen beiden Autobahnen liegt Willingen?

   _____

2. Welche Stadt liegt direkt östlich von Willingen?

   _____

3. Was ist die Telefonnummer vom Skiverleih Udo Nackas?

   _____

4. Welche Vorwahl muss man wählen, wenn man aus dem Ausland anruft?

   _____

5. Wie viele Skischulen gibt es in Willingen?

   _____

6. Welche Postleitzahl hat Willingen?

   _____

7. Wo ist der Skiverleih WiWa?

   _____

8. In wie vielen Skischulen kann man Snowboards bekommen?

   _____

## 7 Complete each sentence using an appropriate noun including the article.

1. Können Sie bei _____ warten?

2. Viele Jugendliche stehen schon früh bei _____.

3. Wir kommen um ein Uhr aus _____.

4. Um wie viel Uhr geht ihr zu _____?

5. Ich kaufe außer _____ auch noch einen Rechner.

6. Bist du schon seit _____ in Europa?

7. Nach _____ fahren wir nach Hause.

8. Wann wirst du etwas von _____ hören?

# KAPITEL 10

## Lektion B

**8** *Wie heißen die Körperteile?* **Write each noun including the article.**

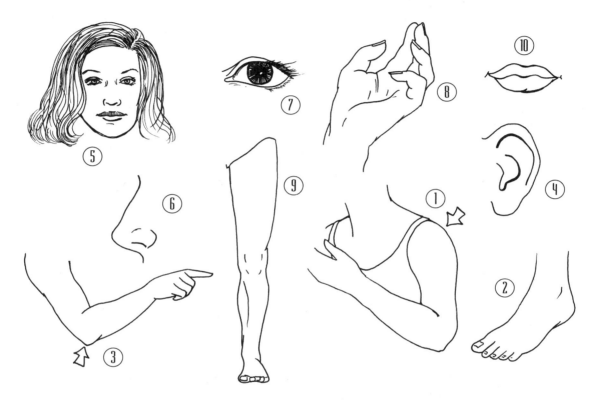

1. _____

2. _____

3. _____

4. _____

5. _____

6. _____

7. _____

8. _____

9. _____

10. _____

**9** *Was fehlt hier?* **Complete the sentences using the correct forms of the verbs listed. Use each verb only once.**

| schießen | gehen | probieren | helfen | brauchen |
| passen | tun | meinen | gefallen | spielen |

1. Der Fußball _____ Peter gut.

2. Es _____ mir sehr Leid.

3. Komm, _____ wir doch weiter!

4. Bitte, _____ auf!

5. Ich _____ dir gern mit deinen Hausaufgaben.

6. Schnell Peter, _____ den Ball zu mir!

7. Dieser Ball _____ noch viel Luft.

8. _____ du, wir sollen jetzt Fußball spielen?

9. Es _____ mir jetzt besser.

10. Warum _____ wir diesen Ball nicht aus?

**10** **Supply the German equivalent for the words given in parentheses.**

1. Kannst du *(your father)* _____ bei der Arbeit helfen?

2. Das Mittagessen in der Schulcafeteria schmeckt *(the girls and boys)* _____ heute gut.

3. Wir glauben *(the woman)* _____ nicht.

4. Wie gefällt *(her boyfriend)* _____ das Fahrrad?

5. Der Mantel steht *(my mother)* _____ nicht schlecht.

6. Passt der Pulli *(his brother)* _____?

7. Es tut *(my sister)* _____ Leid, dass sie nicht mitkommen kann.

8. Tut *(the child)* _____ der Fuß noch weh?

11  *Die Bundesliga.* The standings shown in the table are those of the German national soccer league teams after the game *Mönchengladbach – Dortmund* as described in the *Lesestück.* Here are some words and abbreviations you may need to know: *Punkte* points; *Tore* goals; *Diff./Differenz* difference between number of goals for and against; *Sp./Spiele* games; *G./Gewonnen* games won; *U./Unentschieden* games tied; *V./Verloren* games lost; *auswärts* away from home. Answer the questions that follow. Which team(s)...

| Bundesliga | Punkte | Tore | Diff. | Sp. | G. | U. | V. | zu Hause Punkte | Tore | G. | U. | V. | auswärts Punkte | Tore | G. | U. | V. |
|---|---|---|---|---|---|---|---|---|---|---|---|---|---|---|---|---|---|
| 1. Kaiserslautern | 24 | 23:10 | +13 | 9 | 8 | 0 | 1 | 15 | 14:6 | 5 | 0 | 0 | 9 | 9:4 | 3 | 0 | 1 |
| 2. Bayern | 22 | 21:3 | +18 | 9 | 7 | 1 | 1 | 12 | 10:0 | 4 | 0 | 0 | 10 | 11:3 | 3 | 1 | 1 |
| 3. Leverkusen | 21 | 21:10 | +11 | 9 | 6 | 3 | 0 | 10 | 10:4 | 3 | 1 | 0 | 11 | 11:6 | 3 | 2 | 0 |
| 4. Dortmund | 19 | 15:6 | +9 | 9 | 6 | 1 | 2 | 7 | 7:3 | 2 | 1 | 1 | 12 | 8:3 | 4 | 0 | 1 |
| 5. Stuttgart | 15 | 11:9 | +2 | 9 | 4 | 3 | 2 | 9 | 5:1 | 2 | 3 | 0 | 6 | 6:8 | 2 | 0 | 2 |
| 6. Schalke | 14 | 11:12 | -1 | 9 | 4 | 2 | 3 | 10 | 9:4 | 3 | 1 | 0 | 4 | 2:8 | 1 | 1 | 3 |
| 7. Bremen | 11 | 11:11 | 0 | 8 | 3 | 2 | 3 | 7 | 6:6 | 2 | 1 | 1 | 4 | 5:5 | 1 | 1 | 2 |
| 8. Cottbus | 11 | 12:16 | -4 | 9 | 3 | 2 | 4 | 7 | 7:9 | 2 | 1 | 2 | 4 | 5:7 | 1 | 1 | 2 |
| 9. Hertha BSC | 11 | 11:15 | -4 | 9 | 3 | 2 | 4 | 6 | 7:6 | 2 | 0 | 2 | 5 | 4:9 | 1 | 2 | 2 |
| 10. 1860 München | 11 | 11:18 | -7 | 9 | 3 | 2 | 4 | 7 | 5:11 | 2 | 1 | 2 | 4 | 6:7 | 1 | 1 | 2 |
| 11. Hamburger SV | 9 | 13:14 | -1 | 9 | 2 | 3 | 4 | 7 | 11:10 | 2 | 1 | 2 | 2 | 2:4 | 0 | 2 | 2 |
| 12. Mönchengladbach | 9 | 11:12 | -1 | 9 | 2 | 3 | 4 | 5 | 4:5 | 1 | 2 | 2 | 4 | 7:7 | 1 | 1 | 2 |
| 13. Freiburg | 9 | 11:14 | -3 | 9 | 2 | 3 | 4 | 8 | 9:6 | 2 | 2 | 1 | 1 | 2:8 | 0 | 1 | 3 |
| 14. Köln | 8 | 7:11 | -4 | 8 | 2 | 2 | 4 | 6 | 5:5 | 2 | 0 | 2 | 2 | 2:6 | 0 | 2 | 2 |
| 15. Nürnberg | 7 | 6:11 | -5 | 8 | 2 | 1 | 5 | 4 | 4:6 | 1 | 1 | 2 | 3 | 2:5 | 1 | 0 | 3 |
| 16. Wolfsburg | 6 | 9:15 | -6 | 8 | 1 | 3 | 4 | 5 | 4:4 | 1 | 2 | 1 | 1 | 5:11 | 0 | 1 | 3 |
| 17. Rostock | 6 | 7:16 | -9 | 9 | 1 | 3 | 5 | 2 | 2:7 | 0 | 2 | 2 | 4 | 5:9 | 1 | 1 | 3 |
| 18. St.Pauli | 4 | 7:15 | -8 | 9 | 0 | 4 | 5 | 1 | 1:5 | 0 | 1 | 3 | 3 | 6:10 | 0 | 3 | 2 |

1.  ...lost the most games?

_____

2.  ...won the most games away from home?

_____

3.  ...scored the most goals?

_____

4.  ...won no games away from home?

_____

5.  ...didn't lose any games at home?

_____

6.  ...scored the least number of goals away from home?

_____

7.  ...tied no games?

_____

**12** **Complete each sentence based on the *Lesestück*.**

1. Viele Deutsche sehen jede Woche ihre beliebte Mannschaft im Stadion oder im _____.

2. Ein Spiel dauert 90 _____.

3. In der 1. Bundesliga gibt es 18 _____.

4. Es gibt eine _____ von zehn Minuten.

5. Viele Fans haben schon ihre Karten, andere kaufen sie an der _____.

6. An _____ kann man Bratwurst und Cola kaufen.

7. Viele _____ kommen schon lange vor dem Spiel ins Stadion.

8. Nur der _____ darf den Fußball in die Hand nehmen.

9. Die Spieler wollen den Ball ins _____ schießen.

10. Am Ende des Spiels geben sich die Spieler die _____.

**13** **Fill in the appropriate pronouns given in parentheses.**

1. Wie geht es *(you)* _____, Herr Köhler?

2. Tut es *(them)* _____ nicht Leid, dass sie zu spät kommen?

3. Ich kann *(him)* _____ wirklich nicht glauben.

4. Wie passt *(her)* _____ der Mantel?

5. Rolf, sollen wir *(you)* _____ bei den Hausaufgaben helfen?

6. Der Anzug steht *(me)* _____ ganz toll.

7. Bring *(us)* _____ doch die Zeitung!

8. Wie gefällt *(you)* _____ dieses Video, Anne und Katja?

## 14 Ergänze diese beiden Dialoge!

A:     Willst du Fußball spielen?

B:     _____

A:     Wir spielen auf dem Fußballplatz.

B:     _____

A:     Wir sind immer zehn oder zwölf Spieler.

B:     _____

A:     So gegen vier Uhr.

B:     _____

A:     Nein, wir haben zwei Bälle.

B:     _____

A:     Gut, wir spielen bestimmt zwei Stunden.

*** 

C:     _____

D:     Tag! Was machst du denn jetzt?

C:     _____

D:     Ich spiele Tennis auch sehr gern.

C:     _____

D:     Ja, gut. Wann soll ich auf dem Tennisplatz sein?

C:     _____

D:     Ja, das geht.

C:     _____

D:     Tschüs.

## 15 *Kreuzworträtsel*

## WAAGERECHT

3. Viele Fans bringen ___ ins Stadion.

4. Kannst du mit deinen Augen nicht gut ___?

6. Nur der Torwart ___ den Ball in die Hand nehmen.

7. Robert wünscht sich ___ zu seinem Geburtstag.

8. Man spielt diesen Sport mit einem kleinen weißen Ball.

9. Die Mönchengladbacher spielen gegen die Dortmunder in einem ___.

11. Am Ende ___ es 2:1.

13. Fußball ist in Deutschland der ___.

15. Ein Fußballspiel ___ 90 Minuten.

17. Kurz vor dem Spielende gibt es einen ___.

18. Die Spieler versuchen, den Ball ins ___ zu schießen.

## SENKRECHT

1. An einem ___ kann man Bratwurst und Hamburger kaufen.

2. Was macht ihr im Sommer? Wir ___ gern in den Bergen.

3. Wie kommt ihr in die Stadt? Wir ___ mit dem Rad.

5. Nach 45 Minuten gibt es eine ___.

10. Achims Schwester möchte zum ___ einen Tennisschläger.

11. Welche ___ treibt ihr? Fußball oder Tennis?

12. Manche Zuschauer ___ bunte Hemden.

14. Die Kinder ___ im Winter Schlittschuh.

16. Man hört mit dem ___.

**16** ***Was weißt du von diesem Kapitel?*** **Complete each sentence with a word that you'll most likely find in this chapter. The first letters, when read in sequence, will identify the major soccer league in Germany.**

1. Man braucht ihn beim Fußballspiel. _____

2. Da steht, wie spät es ist. _____

3. Es ist ein Körperteil zwischen *(between)* dem Mund und der Stirn.

   _____

4. Mönchengladbach spielt gegen diese Mannschaft. _____

5. In diesem Sport laufen beide Mannschaften auf Schlittschuhen.

   _____

6. Da sehen viele Zuschauer ein Fußballspiel. _____

7. Achim sagt, dass der Fußball das noch braucht. _____

8. Dort kann man Hamburger, Bratwurst und Cola kaufen.

   _____

9. In diesem Sport hat man ein paar Schläger. Man läuft sehr weit und schießt

   den Ball 100 bis 300 Meter. _____

10. Er ist zwischen der Schulter und der Hand. _____

# KAPITEL 11

## Lektion A

**1** *Wie heißen diese Verkehrsmittel?* **Write the article and the plural form for each item pictured.**

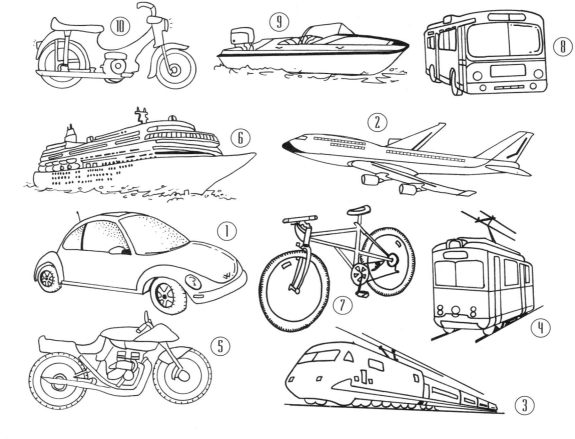

1. _____

2. _____

3. _____

4. _____

5. _____

6. _____

7. _____

8. _____

9. _____

10. _____

**2** Ten different modes of transportation are hidden in the word find. The letters may go backward or forward; they may go up, down, across or diagonally. However, they go only one way in any one word. (Note: ß = SS)

| E | Q | P | R | O | P | O | T | E | S | T | H | Z | Y |
|---|---|---|---|---|---|---|---|---|---|---|---|---|---|
| F | N | H | A | B | N | E | S | S | A | R | T | S | G |
| R | O | F | A | H | R | R | A | D | G | H | I | J | P |
| K | R | S | P | T | Z | Y | B | U | S | W | X | B | C |
| D | L | S | M | N | P | O | E | O | S | O | N | S | P |
| W | H | C | O | I | R | Z | K | H | O | A | W | R | E |
| Y | U | H | A | O | G | U | Z | G | O | T | O | D | D |
| A | Y | I | S | U | I | E | R | O | D | O | S | B | E |
| T | T | F | L | U | T | E | P | T | E | T | L | M | P |
| T | I | F | M | O | T | O | R | R | A | D | Q | U | O |
| S | A | M | X | Y | I | F | U | A | I | R | T | E | M |

**3** *Was fehlt hier?* **Complete the sentences using the correct forms of the verbs listed. Use each verb only once.**

schaffen  machen  fliegen  sein  kommen  kaufen
dauern  fahren  gehen  stehen  nehmen  sehen  steigen

1. _____ du mit dem Bus oder _____ du mit dem Flugzeug von Hamburg nach München.

2. Wohin _____ Sie dieses Jahr im Sommer Ihre Reise?

3. _____ ihr zu Fuß zum Bahnhof?

4. Wann _____ du zu mir rüber?

5. Welches Verkehrsmittel _____ ihr? Den Zug.

6. Mit der U-Bahn _____ es nicht sehr lange, bis wir bei euch sind.

7. Wirst du die Karten heute _____? Nein, ich hole sie morgen im Bahnhof.

8. Fahrt ihr mit dem Zug direkt nach Wien? Nein, wir _____ in Salzburg um.

9. Auf dem Fahrplan _____, um wie viel Uhr die Züge abfahren.

10. Wann geht's denn los? Einen Moment, ich _____ gleich auf dem Fahrplan nach.

11. _____ ihr das Schiff noch? Ja, wir haben noch fünf Minuten Zeit, bis es abfährt.

12. Zu Fuß _____ es zu weit zum See.

Name _____ Datum _____

**4** Write the appropriate present perfect form of the verb given in parentheses.

1. (hören) _____ ihr die Musik _____?

2. (jubeln) Die Jugendlichen _____ viel _____.

3. (kaufen) Wo _____ du deinen Computer

   _____?

4. (regnen) Es _____ gestern _____.

5. (spülen) Ich _____ das Geschirr _____.

6. (schmecken) Wie _____ das Essen _____?

7. (besuchen) Mein Onkel _____ uns im Juni

   _____.

8. (schicken) Wir _____ ihr eine Karte _____.

9. (schaffen) _____ ihr die Arbeit am Montag

   _____?

10. (dauern) Wie viele Stunden _____ euere Reise

    _____?

**5** Complete each sentence using the appropriate verb from the list below in the present perfect tense. You will not use all the verbs listed.

| sammeln | dauern | mähen | danken | machen | warten |
| spielen | wandern | regnen | besuchen | schenken | glauben |

1. Was habt ihr nach der Schule _____?

2. Ich habe den Rasen _____.

3. Bist du im Sommer in den Bergen _____?

4. Nein, es hat jeden Tag _____

5. Haben Gerd und Rudi am Montag Fußball _____?

6. Nein, sie haben ihre Freunde _____.

7. Wer hat dir alle diese Briefmarken _____?

8. Ich habe sie schon ein paar Jahre _____.

9. Hat Dieter lange vor dem Kino auf seine Freunde _____?

10. Nein, es hat nur drei Minuten _____.

**6** *Erzähl, wie die Geburtstagsparty gewesen ist!* **Rewrite the story in the present perfect tense.**

1. Wir warten schon lange auf diesen Tag.

   _____

2. Am Samstag machen wir bei Joachim eine Party.

   _____

3. Joachim wünscht sich von seinen Eltern eine Uhr.

   _____

4. Seine Oma schickt ihm ein Geschenk.

   _____

5. Am Samstag hören ein paar Jugendliche tolle Musik.

   _____

6. Ein paar Jungen und Mädchen tanzen.

   _____

7. Andere spielen Karten.

   _____

8. Joachims Mutter deckt den Tisch.

   _____

9. Das Abendessen schmeckt sehr gut.

   _____

10. Die Party dauert bis spät am Abend.

   _____

**7** *Der Zug von Frankfurt nach Zürich.* **As you have learned from the textbook dialog, the Hoffmanns are taking a train from Frankfurt to Zürich. Look at the train schedule below and answer the questions.**

## Frankfurt Hbf (tief) → **Zürich HB**

| Ab | Zug | | Umsteigen | An | Ab | Zug | | | An | Verkehrstage |
|----|-----|--|-----------|----|----|-----|--|--|----|--------------|
| 8.32 | S 9 | | F-Flugh Regiobf | 8.42 | | | | | | 03 |
| | | | F-Flugh Fernbf | | 8.57 | IC | 609 | | | |
| | | | Basel SBB | 11.46 | 11.53 | IR | 1771 | | 13.00 | |
| 8.49 | ICE | 691 ⅼ | Mannheim Hbf | 9.26 | 9.35 | IC | 609 | | | 06 |
| | | | Basel SBB | 11.46 | 12.07 | IC | 771 | | 12.58 | |
| 8.49 | ICE | 693 ⅼ | Mannheim Hbf | 9.26 | 9.35 | IC | 609 | | | 07 |
| | | | Basel SBB | 11.46 | 11.53 | IR | 1771 | | 13.00 | |
| 9.32 | S 8 | | F-Flugh Regiobf | 9.42 | | | | | | 02 |
| | | | F-Flugh Fernbf | | 9.57 | EC | 5 | ⅼ | | |
| | | | Basel SBB | 12.46 | 13.07 | IC | 773 | | 13.58 | |
| 9.32 | S 9 | | F-Flugh Regiobf | 9.42 | | | | | | 03 |
| | | | F-Flugh Fernbf | | 9.57 | EC | 5 | ⅼ | | |
| | | | Basel SBB | 12.46 | 13.07 | IC | 773 | | 13.58 | |
| 10.05 | ICE | 775 ⅼ | Basel SBB | 12.55 | 13.07 | IC | 773 | | 13.58 | täglich 01 |
| 10.32 | S 8 | | F-Flugh Regiobf | 10.42 | | | | | | 02 |
| | | | F-Flugh Fernbf | | 10.57 | EC | 103 | ⅼ | 14.58 | |
| 10.32 | S 9 | | F-Flugh Regiobf | 10.42 | | | | | | 03 |
| | | | F-Flugh Fernbf | | 10.57 | EC | 103 | ⅼ | 14.58 | |
| 10.49 | ICE | 591 ⅼ | Mannheim Hbf | 11.26 | 11.35 | EC | 103 | ⅼ | 14.58 | täglich 01 |
| 11.32 | S 8 | | F-Flugh Regiobf | 11.42 | | | | | | 02 |
| | | | F-Flugh Fernbf | | 11.57 | EC | 9 | ⅼ | | |
| | | | Basel SBB | 14.46 | 15.07 | IC | 777 | | 15.58 | |
| 11.32 | S 9 | | F-Flugh Regiobf | 11.42 | | | | | | 03 |
| | | | F-Flugh Fernbf | | 11.57 | EC | 9 | ⅼ | | |
| | | | Basel SBB | 14.46 | 15.07 | IC | 777 | | 15.58 | |
| 12.05 | ICE | 73 ⅼ | Basel SBB | 14.55 | 15.07 | IC | 777 | | 15.58 | täglich 01 |
| 12.32 | S 8 | | F-Flugh Regiobf | 12.42 | | | | | | 02 |
| | | | F-Flugh Fernbf | | 12.57 | EC | 3 | ⅼ | 16.58 | |
| 12.32 | S 9 | | F-Flugh Regiobf | 12.42 | | | | | | 03 |
| | | | F-Flugh Fernbf | | 12.57 | EC | 3 | ⅼ | 16.58 | |
| 12.49 | ICE | 593 ⅼ | Mannheim Hbf | 13.26 | 13.35 | EC | 3 | ⅼ | 16.58 | täglich 01 |
| 13.32 | S 8 | | F-Flugh Regiobf | 13.42 | | | | | | 02 |
| | | | F-Flugh Fernbf | | 13.57 | EC | 109 | ⅼ | | |
| | | | Basel SBB | 16.46 | 17.07 | IC | 783 | | 17.58 | |
| 13.32 | S 9 | | F-Flugh Regiobf | 13.42 | | | | | | 03 |
| | | | F-Flugh Fernbf | | 13.57 | EC | 109 | ⅼ | | |
| | | | Basel SBB | 16.46 | 17.07 | IC | 783 | | 17.58 | |
| 14.05 | ICE | 71 ⅼ | Basel SBB | 16.55 | 17.07 | IC | 783 | | 17.58 | täglich 01 |
| 14.32 | S 8 | | F-Flugh Regiobf | 14.42 | | | | | | 05 |
| | | | F-Flugh Fernbf | | 14.57 | EC | 105 | ⅼ | | |
| | | | Basel SBB | 17.46 | 18.07 | IC | 787 | | 18.58 | |
| 14.32 | S 8 | | F-Flugh Regiobf | 14.42 | | | | | | 02 |
| | | | F-Flugh Fernbf | | 14.57 | EC | 105 | ⅼ | | |
| | | | Basel SBB | 17.46 | 17.53 | IR | 1785 | | 19.00 | |
| 14.32 | S 9 | | F-Flugh Regiobf | 14.42 | | | | | | 03 |
| | | | F-Flugh Fernbf | | 14.57 | EC | 105 | ⅼ | | |
| | | | Basel SBB | 17.46 | 17.53 | IR | 1785 | | 19.00 | |
| 14.49 | ICE | 595 ⅼ | Mannheim Hbf | 15.26 | 15.35 | EC | 105 | ⅼ | | 06 |
| | | | Basel SBB | 17.46 | 18.07 | IC | 787 | | 18.58 | |
| 14.49 | ICE | 595 ⅼ | Mannheim Hbf | 15.26 | 15.35 | EC | 105 | ⅼ | | täglich 01 |
| | | | Basel SBB | 17.46 | 17.53 | IR | 1785 | | 19.00 | |
| 15.32 | S 8 | | F-Flugh Regiobf | 15.42 | | | | | | 02 |
| | | | F-Flugh Fernbf | | 15.57 | IC | 505 | ⅼ | | |
| | | | Basel SBB | 18.46 | 18.53 | EC | 97 | | 20.00 | |
| 15.32 | S 9 | | F-Flugh Regiobf | 15.42 | | | | | | 03 |
| | | | F-Flugh Fernbf | | 15.57 | IC | 505 | ⅼ | | |
| | | | Basel SBB | 18.46 | 18.53 | EC | 97 | | 20.00 | |
| 16.05 | ICE | 77 ⅼ | | | | | | | 19.58 | täglich 01 |
| 16.32 | S 8 | | F-Flugh Regiobf | 16.42 | | | | | | 02 |
| | | | F-Flugh Fernbf | | 16.57 | IC | 707 | ⅼ | | |
| | | | Basel SBB | 19.46 | 19.53 | IR | 1789 | | 21.00 | |
| 16.32 | S 9 | | F-Flugh Regiobf | 16.42 | | | | | | 03 |
| | | | F-Flugh Fernbf | | 16.57 | IC | 707 | ⅼ | | |
| | | | Basel SBB | 19.46 | 19.53 | IR | 1789 | | 21.00 | |

1. Um wie viel Uhr kommen Hoffmanns in Basel an?

   _____

2. Wie oft in der Woche fährt dieser Zug um diese Zeit?

   _____

3. Wie viele Minuten haben Hoffmanns in Basel, in den Zug nach Zürich
   umzusteigen?

   _____

4. Gibt es in diesem Zug ein Restaurant?

   _____

5. Um wie viel Uhr fährt der erste ICE-Zug nach Zürich?

   _____

6. Eine andere Familie will so gegen acht Uhr am Abend mit dem schnellsten
   Zug in Zürich ankommen. Um wie viel Uhr fährt die Familie von Frankfurt
   ab?

   _____

7. Angelika will um 14.49 Uhr mit dem Zug von Frankfurt nach Mannheim
   fahren. Wie lange dauert die Reise dorthin?

   _____

8. Wie lange dauert es mit der S-Bahn vom Frankfurter Flughafen
   Regionalbahnhof (F-Flugh Regiobf) zum Fernbahnhof (F-Flugh Fernbf)?

   _____

**8** *Von Dresden nach Wiesbaden.* **When traveling in Germany, you can pick up schedules such as the one shown below at major train stations. Look at the schedule of trains going between Dresden and Frankfurt and then choose the most appropriate ending for each beginning.**

# Dresden Hbf
## → **Wiesbaden Hbf**

| Ab | Zug | | Umsteigen | An | Ab | Zug | | An | Verkehrstage |
|---|---|---|---|---|---|---|---|---|---|
| 5.25 | RE 17442 | | Leipzig Hbf<br>Frankfurt(M)Hbf | 7.02<br>10.36 | 7.22<br>10.53 | ICE 1654<br>RE 15010 | ¶¶ | <br>11.26 | täglich |
| 5.53 | IC 527 | ⚌ | Leipzig Hbf<br>Frankfurt(M)Hbf | 7.05<br>10.36 | 7.22<br>10.53 | ICE 1654<br>RE 15010 | ¶¶ | <br>11.26 | 01 |
| 5.55 | IC 527 | ⚌ | Leipzig Hbf<br>Frankfurt(M)Hbf | 7.17<br>10.36 | 7.22<br>10.53 | ICE 1654<br>RE 15010 | ¶¶ | <br>11.26 | 02 |
| 6.52 | IR 2038 | ⚌ | Halle(Saale)Hbf<br>Frankfurt(M)Hbf<br>Frankf Hbf (tief) | 9.00<br>13.57 | 9.54<br><br>14.12 | IR 2007<br><br>Ⓢ 1 | ⚌ | <br><br>14.52 | 03 |
| 7.25 | RE 17446 | | Leipzig Hbf<br>Frankfurt(M)Hbf | 9.02<br>12.36 | 9.22<br>12.53 | ICE 1652<br>RE 15014 | ¶¶ | <br>13.26 | täglich |
| 8.11 | ICE 1652 | ¶¶ | Frankfurt(M)Hbf | 12.36 | 12.53 | RE 15014 | | 13.26 | Mo - Sa 04 |
| 8.52 | IR 2334 | ⚌ | Halle(Saale)Hbf<br>Frankfurt(M)Hbf<br>Frankf Hbf (tief) | 11.00<br>15.57 | 11.54<br><br>16.12 | IR 2009<br><br>Ⓢ 1 | ⚌ | <br><br>16.52 | 03 |
| 10.11 | ICE 1650 | ¶¶ | Frankfurt(M)Hbf | 14.36 | 14.53 | RE 15018 | | 15.26 | täglich |
| 10.52 | IR 2034 | | Halle(Saale)Hbf<br>Frankfurt(M)Hbf<br>Frankf Hbf (tief) | 13.00<br>17.57 | 13.54<br><br>18.12 | IR 2101<br><br>Ⓢ 1 | ⚌ | <br><br>18.52 | 03 |
| 12.11 | ICE 1558 | ¶¶ | Frankfurt(M)Hbf | 16.36 | 16.53 | RE 15026 | | 17.26 | täglich |
| 12.52 | IR 2332 | ⚌ | Halle(Saale)Hbf<br>Frankfurt(M)Hbf<br>Frankf Hbf (tief) | 15.00<br>19.57 | 15.54<br><br>20.12 | IR 2103<br><br>Ⓢ 1 | ⚌ | <br><br>20.52 | 05 |
| 14.11 | ICE 1556 | ¶¶ | Frankfurt(M)Hbf | 18.36 | 18.53 | RE 15032 | | 19.26 | täglich |
| 16.11 | ICE 1554 | ¶¶ | Frankfurt(M)Hbf<br>Mainz Hbf | 20.36<br>21.13 | 20.45<br>21.19 | ICE 822<br>RB 15850 | ¶¶ | <br>21.30 | täglich |
| 16.11 | ICE 1554 | ¶¶ | Frankfurt(M)Hbf<br>Frankf Hbf (tief) | 20.36 | <br>21.12 | <br>Ⓢ 1 | | <br>21.52 | täglich |
| 18.11 | ICE 1552 | ¶¶ | Frankfurt(M)Hbf<br>Frankf Hbf (tief) | 22.39 | <br>23.12 | <br>Ⓢ 1 | | <br>23.52 | täglich 06 |

_____ 1. ICE-Zug 1558 kommt

_____ 2. Der IR-Zug 2334 fährt

_____ 3. Der ICE-Zug 1554 fährt

_____ 4. Der IC-Zug 527 kommt

_____ 5. Der RE-Zug 17446 fährt

_____ 6. Der ICE-Zug 1650 fährt

_____ 7. Der ICE-Zug 1556 fährt

_____ 8. Der RE-Zug 17442 ist

A. aus Leipzig.

B. um 9.22 von Leipzig ab.

C. so gegen zwei Uhr am Nachmittag von Dresden ab.

D. um 16.36 Uhr in Frankfurt an.

E. der erste Zug aus Dresden in Leipzig.

F. von Halle ab.

G. zuerst nach Frankfurt und dann weiter nach Mainz.

H. direkt von Dresden nach Frankfurt.

# KAPITEL 11

## Lektion B

**9** *Was passt hier?* **You may use each word or phrase only once.**

| | |
|---|---|
| _____ 1. Zur Stadtmitte fahren Sie nicht, gehen Sie lieber | A. die Post |
| _____ 2. Das Kaufhaus finden Sie gleich | B. geben |
| _____ 3. Ich kann Ihnen Auskunft | C. der Pizzeria |
| _____ 4. Ich bin fremd | D. alle da drüben |
| _____ 5. Das Museum ist ganz in | E. der Nähe |
| _____ 6. Zum Bahnhof gehen Sie am Kaufhaus | F. auf der rechten Seite neben dem Bahnhof |
| _____ 7. Nach fünf Minuten kommen Sie | G. hier |
| _____ 8. An der nächsten Ecke sehen Sie | H. vorbei |
| _____ 9. Das Geschäft ist gleich links von | I. zum Café |
| _____ 10. Die Kofferkulis stehen | J. zu Fuß |

**10** *Wie kommt man dahin?* **This is the city map for Suhl, located in central Germany. Imagine that you are working at an information office right at the market square *(Marktplatz)*. Several tourists ask you how to get to certain places. Describe to them how they would get there.** *Auf Deutsch, bitte!*

# Damit Sie alles finden

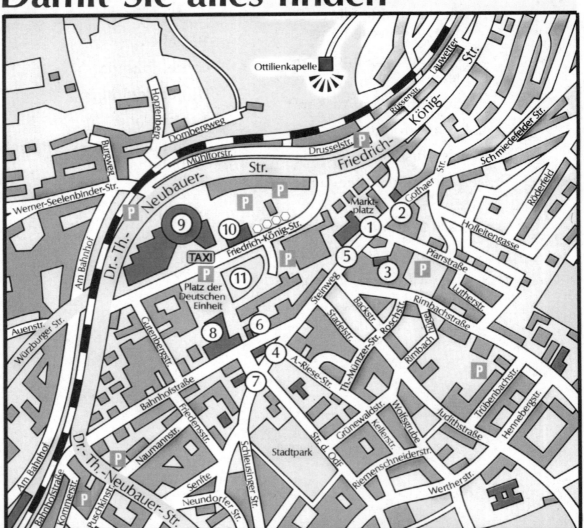

**Suhler Innenstadtplan**

1. Rathaus am Marktplatz (mit Waffenschmieddenkmal)
2. Amt für Tourismus und Sport
3. Hauptkirche St. Marien
4. Kreuzkirche
5. Steinweg
6. Polizei
7. Post
8. Haus „Philharmonie" mit Kunstkabinett, Bibliothek und Kino
9. Congress Centrum Suhl
10. Waffenmuseum mit historischem Fachwerkhaus
11. Herrenteich

*Beispiel:* Wie komme ich zum Herrenteich?

Gehen Sie einfach den Steinweg entlang, dann weiter auf der Bahnhofstraße. Beim Platz der Deutschen Einheit ist rechts der Herrenteich.

1. Wie komme ich zur Post?

   _____

2. Wo ist Haus „Philharmonie"?

   _____

3. Ist das Rathaus hier in der Nähe?

   _____

4. Können Sie mir sagen, wo das Congress Centrum Suhl ist?

   _____

   _____

5. Ich muss zur Polizei. Wie komme ich dorthin?

   _____

   _____

6. Wo ist die Hauptkirche St. Marien?

   _____

7. Wissen Sie, wo die Lutherstraße ist?

   _____

   _____

8. Wo ist die Gutenbergstraße, bitte?

   _____

   _____

**11** *Können Sie mir sagen, wie ich dorthin komme?* Complete the following two dialogs in which you need to give tourists directions. In the first dialog, you are standing at the subway station marked with a **U** at *Zschokkestraße*. In the second dialog, you are on *Dingolfinger Straße*. (Note that *m* means *Meter*, which is slightly longer than a yard.)

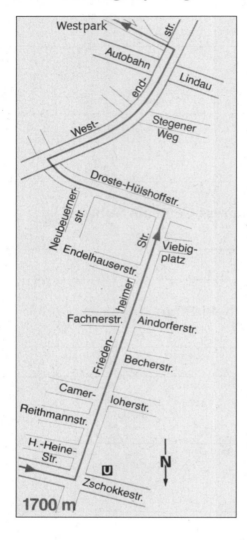
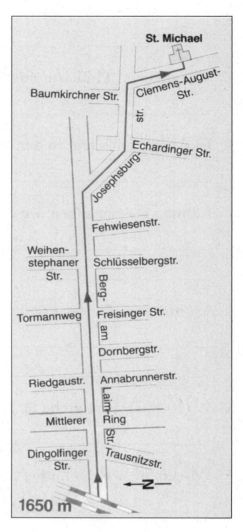

*Tourist:* Können Sie mir sagen, wie ich zum Westpark komme?

*Du:* _____

*Tourist:* Zu Fuß.

*Du:* _____

*Tourist:* Nein, ich habe keine Zeit. Wie weit ist es von hier?

*Du:* _____

*Tourist:* Wie lange dauert das ungefähr?

*Du:* _____

*Tourist:* Wie muss ich dorthin zu Fuß gehen?

*Du:* _____

*Tourist:* Und dann weiter von der Droste-Hülshoffstraße?

*Du:* _____

_____

*Tourist:* Bin ich in der Westendstraße dann gleich beim Park?

*Du:* _____

_____

*Tourist:* Danke.

***

*Du:* Bitte schön?

*Tourist:* _____

*Du:* Baumkirchner Straße? Ja, das ist ganz leicht.

*Tourist:* _____

*Du:* Mit dem Auto geht es natürlich schnell.

*Tourist:* _____

*Du:* Nur fünf Minuten.

*Tourist:* _____

*Du:* Das ist ja gleich da drüben. Sie fahren auf die Berg-am-Laim Straße.

*Tourist:* _____

*Du:* Nach rechts.

*Tourist:* _____

*Du:* Acht Ecken. Die Berg-am-Laim Straße geht in die Josephsburgstraße.

*Tourist:* _____

*Du:* Ja, gleich nach der Echardinger Straße kommt die Baumkirchner Straße links.

*Tourist:* Danke.

**12** *Was fehlt hier?* **Complete each sentence by adding the missing prefix.**

1. Um wie viel Uhr fährt der Zug nach Köln _____?

2. Warum nimmst du immer so viel Gepäck _____?

3. Komm, schnell! Steigen wir gleich in die U-Bahn _____!

4. Fahren Sie direkt von Stuttgart nach Bremen? Nein, wir steigen in Frankfurt _____.

5. Zur Post gehen Sie am Bahnhof _____.

6. Zum Kaufhaus? Biegen Sie hier rechts _____!

7. Siehst du auf dem Fahrplan _____?

8. Der Zug aus Hannover kommt auf Gleis fünf _____.

**13** *Ergänze den Dialog zwischen Gabi und Martina!* **Write the appropriate present perfect form of the verb given in parentheses.**

*Gabi:* Wo bist du denn gestern (sein) _____?

*Martina:* Ich bin zu meiner Cousine (fahren) _____.

*Gabi:* Hat sie dich (einladen) _____?

*Martina:* Ja, sie hat mir vor zwei Wochen einen Brief (schreiben)

_____.

*Gabi:* Ist dein Bruder auch (mitkommen) _____?

*Martina:* Nein, er ist zu Hause (bleiben) _____.

*Gabi:* Hat die Sonne die ganze Zeit (scheinen) _____?

*Martina:* Ja, wir sind fast jeden Tag zum See (gehen) _____.

*Gabi:* Hat es euch da (gefallen) _____?

*Martina:* Ja sehr. Wir sind dort (schwimmen) _____ und

haben lange am Strand (sitzen) _____.

**14** *Was haben Hoffmanns gemacht?* **The two dialogs in this chapter have described Mr. and Mrs. Hoffmann's train trip. Complete the following narrative that summarizes their travel experiences.**

Herr und Frau Hoffmann sind mit der U-Bahn zum Bahnhof

_____. Dort haben sie auf einem Fahrplan

_____, wann der Zug nach Zürich abfahren wird. Auf

dem Fahrplan hat _____, dass der Zug kurz nach zwölf

abfährt. Herr Hoffmann hat die Fahrkarten im Internet

_____. Das hat nicht lange _____.


Eine Dame hat Hoffmanns _____, wo sie Kofferkulis

bekommen können. Herr Hoffmann hat dann gleich einen Kofferkuli für das

Gepäck _____. Frau Hoffmann hat

_____, dass sie zu viel Gepäck

_____ haben. Frau Hoffmanns Schwester hat beide für

14 Tage _____. Herr und Frau Hoffmann sind vor ein

paar Jahren nur ein paar Tage bei der Schwester _____.

Es hat ihnen bei ihr sehr gut _____. Sie sind zum Gleis

sechs _____. Der Zug ist schon vor ein paar Minuten

_____. Sie sind gleich in den Zug

_____. Vom Gleis sechs sind sie dann

_____.

**15** *Von wem spricht man hier?* **Based on the** *Lesestück,* **determine to whom the following sentences refer.** *Diese Person hat... Diese Personen haben...*

1. einen Vater in einer anderen Stadt. _____

2. das Gutenberg Museum besucht. _____

3. ein Museum in Boppard vorgeschlagen. _____

4. nach Koblenz den Zug genommen. _____

5. gehört, wie die Reise gewesen ist. _____

6. am Bahnsteig auf den Zug aus Mainz gewartet. _____

7. an einem Imbiss etwas gegessen. _____

8. schon lange ihre Reise geplant. _____

9. ein Geschenk bekommen. _____

10. am Schalter gefragt, was man in Boppard sehen kann.

_____

**16** *Wohin hast du eine Reise gemacht?* **Write a short essay in German about a trip that you have taken during the last few years. If you haven't taken a trip, write about an imaginary journey. Your essay should answer the following questions:** *Wann, wohin und mit wem bist du gefahren? Wie lange bist du dort gewesen? Was hast du alles gemacht? Wie hat es dir gefallen?* **Be as creative as possible.**

_____

_____

_____

_____

_____

_____

_____

_____

_____

_____

_____

_____

_____

_____

_____

_____

_____

_____

_____

Name _____     Datum _____

17 *Reisen.* **In the ad you will find four different trips offered by a travel agency. Answer the questions. (Note:** *Schönef.* **= Schönefeld)**

TUI Sonnen Specials!

Jetzt buchen!

**Tunesien/Hammamet** Hotel Mediteranee
✸✸✸ DZ, HP, Bad od. Du., Blk. od. Terr., Kl.
**1 Wo.** m. Flug am 5.4. ab Berlin-Schönef. p. P.
(Verlängerungs-Woche pro Person € 130)                € **349**

**Mallorca/Cala Ratjada** Hotel Diamant
✸✸✸✸ DZ, Halbp., Bad, Balkon, Klimaanl.
**1 Wo.** mit Flug am 7.4. ab Berlin-Schönef. p. P.
(Verlängerungs-Woche pro Person € 120)                € **379**

**Lanzarote/Playa Blanca** Hotel H10 Rubicon Palace
✸✸✸✸✸ DZ, Halbp., Bad, Blk. od. Terr., Kl.
**1 Wo.** mit Flug am 17.3. ab Berlin-Schönef. p. P.       € **599**
(Verlängerungs-Woche pro Person € 320)

**Kreta/Rethymnon** Hotel Golden Beach
✸✸✸✸ Doppelz., HP, Bad, Blk. od. Terr., Kl.
**1 Wo.** m. Flug am 30.3. ab Berlin-Schönef. p. P.        € **659**

**Inklusive: Versicherungsgebühr, Zug zum Flug und TUI Geld zurück-Garantie!**
Noch mehr Angebote in allen Reisebüros mit dem TUI Zeichen, TUI ReiseCentern oder unter **www.tui.de**

TUI

1. Wie viel kostet eine Reise nach Mallorca?

   _____

2. Von welcher Stadt muss man abfliegen *(take off by plane)*?

   _____

3. Wie lange kann man in einem Hotel in Tunesien für den Preis von € 349 übernachten *(stay over night)*?

   _____

4. Wann muss man nach Kreta abfliegen?

   _____

5. Wie viel mehr kostet es, in Lanzarotte eine Woche länger zu bleiben?

   _____

6. In welchem Land ist das Hotel Mediteranee?

   _____

7. Wie viel kostet eine Reise für eine Familie (Vater, Mutter, Junge und Mädchen) zur Insel Kreta?

   _____

8. Von den vier Angeboten *(offers)*, wohin möchtest du? Warum?

   _____

   _____

   _____

**18** *Kreuzworträtsel* **(Note:** *ß* **= SS)**

## WAAGERECHT

1. Der ___ steht auf Gleis sechs.

3. Nina und Cornelia fahren mit einem ___ auf dem Rhein.

4. Cornelia erzählt ___ Mutter von der Reise.

5. Fährst du mit der U-Bahn oder gehst du zu ___?

7. Cornelia ___ ihren Vater in Mainz.

8. Zur Post gehen Sie am Kaufhaus ___.

9. Sie steigen in ___ aus.

11. Der Zug fährt vom Gleis sechs ___.

12. Sie haben die Karten von Boppard nach Mainz an einem Automaten ___.

14. Das Museum ist gleich an der nächsten ___.

16. Biegen Sie ___ ab!

## SENKRECHT

1. Herr und Frau Hoffmann werden ___ Wochen bei Frau Hoffmanns Schwester bleiben.

2. Warum ___ du auf dem Fahrplan nach? Da steht, um wie viel Uhr der Zug abfährt.

3. Sie fahren mit einem Boot auf dem ___.

5. Wie viel kosten die ___ von hier nach Augsburg?

6. Sie ___ in Nürnberg um und fahren mit einem anderen Zug weiter.

7. Cornelia und Nina ___ eine Woche in Mainz.

10. Auf dem Fahrplan steht die ___ und die Abfahrt.

13. Am Schalter hat ihnen eine ___ ein Museum vorgeschlagen.

15. Sie steigen in den Zug ___.

# KAPITEL 12

## Lektion A

1 *Musikinstrumente in Markneukirchen.* The town of Markneukirchen, located in eastern Germany close to the border of the Czech Republic, is known for producing fine musical instruments. Read the ads and then answer the questions.

Name _____ Datum _____

1. What's the name of the store that is about 100 yards from a museum?

   _____

2. Which company is older than 100 years?

   _____

3. Which factory manufactures saxophones?

   _____

4. Where can you purchase classical guitars?

   _____

5. On which street is Jürgen Voigt's shop located?

   _____

6. Who specializes in making, repairing and restoring violins?

   _____

7. What area code would you use to call from outside this town?

   _____

8. How many of these companies use their phone also for fax transmissions?

   _____

## 2  *Wie heißen diese Musikinstrumente?* Write each noun with the appropriate article.

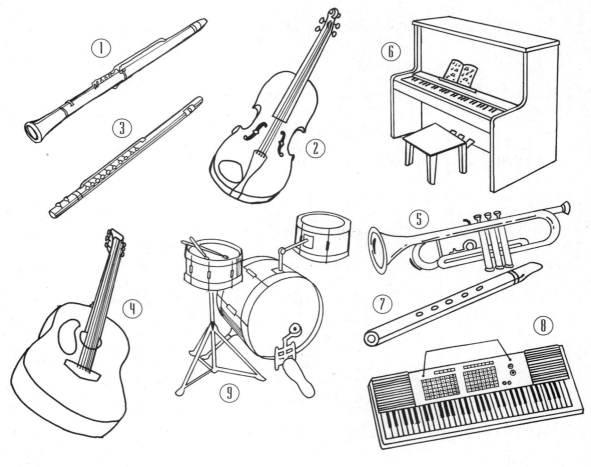

1. _____

2. _____

3. _____

4. _____

5. _____

6. _____

7. _____

8. _____

9. _____

## 3 *Was passt hier?* Find the most approriate ending for each sentence beginning, based on the narrative at the beginning of this chapter.

_____ 1. Katja, Nadine und Simone werden

_____ 2. Heute gibt's

_____ 3. Sie sitzen

_____ 4. Katja bringt

_____ 5. Es macht

_____ 6. Simone sieht

_____ 7. Alle drei Mädchen üben

_____ 8. Simone hört

_____ 9. Nadine und Katja sollen

_____ 10. Am Abend kommen

_____ 11. Simone ruft

_____ 12. Mozart hat

A. lieber CDs

B. heute keinen Spaß

C. „Eine kleine Nachtmusik" komponiert

D. ihre beiden Freundinnen an

E. ein interessantes Fernsehprogramm

F. fern

G. mit ihren Musikinstrumenten rüberkommen

H. etwas von Mozart spielen

I. ein paar Mal

J. am Tisch

K. noch andere Schulfreunde zu Simone rüber

L. ihre Geige mit

**4** *Besondere Konzerte.* **Look at the program and then answer the questions.** *Auf Deutsch, bitte!* **(Note:** *hat komponiert* **has composed;** *stattfinden* **to take place;** *die Postleitzahl* **zip code;** *der Vorname* **first name.)**

# DAS BESONDERE KONZERT IM HERZEN DER ALTSTADT
## A memorable concert in the heart of the old town

Aus dem Programm
### Mai – Oktober

*Wolfgang Amadeus Mozart*
Serenade
»Eine kleine Nachtmusik«

◆

Orchesterkonzert
für Violine, Klarinette oder Klavier

◆

Arien
Sinfonien
Divertimenti

*Johann Strauß*
Walzer
&
Polka

*Mozart Kammerorchester
Salzburg*

W. A. Mozart

Johann Strauß

### 25. MAI – 16. JULI
### 7. SEPT. – 13. OKT.
jeden
**Freitag und Samstag**

## Festival-Office
Anton-Adlgasser-Weg 22 · A-5020 Salzburg
Tel. (0 66 2) **825858** · Fax (0 66 2) **825859**
E-mail: info@mozartfestival.at, Internet: mozartfestival.at

1. Was für Musik hat Johann Strauß komponiert?

   _____

2. An welchen beiden Tagen finden die Konzerte statt?

   _____

3. In welcher Stadt und in welchem Land sind diese Konzerte?

   _____

4. In welchen Jahreszeiten finden die Konzerte statt?

   _____

5. Welche Postleitzahl hat diese Stadt?

   _____

6. Kann man die Konzertkarten nur an der Kasse kaufen?

   _____

7. Was ist Mozarts Vorname?

   _____

8. Welche Musikinstrumente spielen die Musiker im Orchester?

   _____

**5** *Welche Wörter passen hier zusammen?* **Using the words from the following list, form a compound noun for each word listed below and include the article.**

> der Schläger    das Ende    der Kuli    die Mitte    die Liga
>
> die Zeit    die Karte    die Bahn    das Spiel    der Stand
>
> das Instrument    der Teil    der Spüler    das Mittel    der Roller    die Flöte

1. der Block: _____

2. der Computer: _____

3. die Post: _____

4. die Musik: _____

5. der Bund: _____

6. die Straße: _____

7. der Imbiss: _____

8. der Motor: _____

9. die Stadt: _____

10. das Tennis: _____

11. der Koffer: _____

12. der Körper: _____

13. das Geschirr: _____

14. der Verkehr: _____

15. die Woche: _____

16. das Jahr: _____

## 6  Was sind die Gegenteile (*opposites*)?

1. ungefähr: _____

2. alt: _____

3. alles: _____

4. schnell: _____

5. schwarz: _____

6. rechts: _____

7. leicht: _____

8. da: _____

9. früh: _____

10. schlecht: _____

11. drinnen: _____

12. lang: _____

13. kalt: _____

14. mit: _____

15. nach: _____

# KAPITEL 12

## Lektion B

**7** *Was fehlt?* **Complete each sentence based on the dialog in *Lektion B*.**

1. Simones Vater bietet _____.

2. Katjas Geige ist _____.

3. Katja und Nadine wohnen _____.

4. Die Schulfreunde sprechen _____.

5. Simones Vater macht _____.

6. Die drei Mädchen üben _____.

7. Katja und Nadine klingeln. Simone macht _____.

8. Der Kuchen _____.

**8** **Fill in the correct words. The first letters, when read in sequence, spell the name of a musical instrument.**

1. Der _____ ist einer der elf Spieler in einer Fußballmannschaft. Er darf den Ball in die Hand nehmen.

2. Der _____ ist der längste Fluss in Deutschland.

3. Ein _____ ist ein Körperteil. Man braucht es zum Hören.

4. Viele trinken _____ gern. Sie ist weiß.

5. Mit einem Hamburger schmecken _____ immer gut.

6. _____ sind ein Vater und eine Mutter.

7. _____ Sie gern Kaffee?

8. _____ ist sehr kalter Tee.

**9** **Using complete sentences, answer the following questions based on the**
**_Lesestück._**

1. In welcher Stadt wohnen Daniela und Gabriella? Wo liegt diese Stadt?

   _____

2. Wie kommen sie jeden Dienstag zum Tanzstudio?

   _____

3. Sind Daniela und Gabriella Anfänger beim Tanzen?

   _____

4. Was sehen sich beide vor der Tanzstunde an?

   _____

5. Was machen alle Jugendlichen zuerst?

   _____

6. Wie wissen die Tänzer, wie gut sie tanzen?

   _____

7. Was sollen die Tänzer besser machen?

   _____

8. Was werden sie in zwei Wochen machen?

   _____

9. Wer wird dorthin kommen?

   _____

**10** *Gehen wir zum Tanz!* **Look over the ads and then answer the questions.**

1. Wo ist jeden Samstag im Oktober viel los?

   _____

2. In welcher Stadt ist das Tanzcenter Gambrinus?

   _____

3. Wie heißt der DJ aus dem Vogtland?

   _____

4. Wie ist die Faxnummer vom Musikland Zwota?

   _____

5. Welche Postleitzahl (zip code) hat Plauen?

   _____

6. An welchem Tag spielt man in Klingenthal Disco Top Hits?

   _____

7. Wie viele Stunden spielt man in Oberstdorf *Die Chartbreaker der Woche*?

   _____

8. An welchen Tagen ist im Tanzcenter Gambrinus nichts los?

   _____

**11** **Da gibt's immer Musik!** As all over Germany, there are numerous musical events in the Rhine area every year. Look at the announcements and match the events with their respective descriptions.

---

**26.7.** Donnerstag, 19.00 Uhr
Schloss Vollrads, Seebühne (bei Regen um 20.00 Uhr im Kurhaus Wiesbaden)

**„Glenn Miller is back"**
**Swing Time Big Band**

Eine stilechte Bühnenshow mit den unvergesslichen Hits der Swing-Ära, gekrönt von einem Glenn Miller-Special

---

**14.7.** Samstag, 19.00 Uhr (Ende gegen 22.30 Uhr)
Kloster Eberbach, Kreuzgang und verschiedene Räume

**Mozart-Nacht**
**Mozart und die Mannheimer Schule**

Besetzung und Programm s. 13.7.

---

**30.8.** Donnerstag, 20.00 Uhr
Kloster Eberbach, Basilika

**Mozart: Requiem**

SANDRINE PIAU, Sopran · ANNETTE MARKERT, Alt
JAN KOBOW, Tenor · STEPHAN LOGES, Bass
DRESDNER KAMMERCHOR · DRESDNER BAROCKORCHESTER
HANS-CHRISTOPH RADEMANN, Leitung
W. A. Mozart: Vesperae solennes de confessore KV 339

---

**21.7.** Samstag, 20.00 Uhr
Kurhaus Wiesbaden, Friedrich-von-Thiersch-Saal

**Mozart: Die Klavierkonzerte X**
**Ewa Kupiec, Klavier**
**London Mozart Players**
**Howard Shelley, Leitung**

Serenade G-Dur KV 525 „Eine kleine Nachtmusik",
Klavierkonzerte F-Dur KV 413, C-Dur KV 415,
Divertimento D-Dur KV 136 „1. Salzburger Sinfonie"

---

**6.7.** Freitag, 20.00 Uhr
Idstein, Unionskirche

**Chorkunstakademie Moskau**
**Viktor Popov, Leitung**

Aus der Schatzkammer der russischen Chormusik: Werke von
V. Kalinnikow, A. Archangelsky, D. Bortniansky, P. Tschaikowsky,
M. Glinka, G. Swiridow, W. Rubin u. a.

---

**19.8.** Sonntag, 17.00 Uhr (Dauer: 1 Stunde ohne Pause)
Kurhaus Wiesbaden, Friedrich-von-Thiersch-Saal

**Kinderkonzert**
**„Peter und der Wolf"**
**Norbert Blüm, Erzähler**

DRESDNER KAPELLSOLISTEN
HELMUT BRANNY, Leitung
J. Haydn: Sinfonie Es-Dur Hob. I:55
„Der Schulmeister"; S. Prokofjew:
„Peter und der Wolf" op. 67;
Norbert Blüm liest aus seinen
Kinderbüchern

---

**5.8.** Sonntag, 15.30 Uhr (Rückkehr gegen 19.30 Uhr)
MS Wappen von Mainz; Eltville, KD-Anlegestelle

**Riverboat Shuffle**
**Mississippi-Feeling auf dem Rhein**

Verschiedene Jazzformationen spielen auf und unter Deck.
*Die Schiffsgastronomie heißt Sie willkommen!*

---

**21.8.** Dienstag, 20.00 Uhr
Kloster Eberbach, Kreuzgang (bei Regen in der Basilika)

**Prager Kammerorchester**
**Giles Apap, Violine**

J. Haydn: Sinfonie g-Moll Hob. I:83 „La poule";
W. A. Mozart: Violinkonzert Nr. 3 G-Dur KV 216;
C. Saint-Saëns: Havanaise E-Dur op. 83; O. Respighi: „Gli uccelli"

---

_____ 1. Chorkunstakademie Moskau

_____ 2. Mozart: Requiem

_____ 3. Swing Time Big Band

_____ 4. Riverboat Shuffle

_____ 5. Mozart-Nacht

_____ 6. Peter und der Wolf

_____ 7. Die Klavierkonzerte X

_____ 8. Prager Kammerorchester

A. takes place on July 14

B. recreates an atmosphere of the southern part of the United States

C. is performed at the very end of August inside a monastery

D. takes place on a Saturday in Wiesbaden

E. performs at 7 P.M. at a castle outside, weather-permitting, or 8 P.M. inside

F. comes from a neighboring country east of Germany

G. performes as a choir in a church

H. is enjoyed especially by children

## 12 Beende diese beiden Dialoge!

*A:* Möchtest du am Samstag zum Tanz gehen?

*B:* _____

*A:* Hast du am Freitag Abend Zeit?

*B:* _____

*A:* Wir können am Freitag ins Kino gehen.

*B:* _____

*A:* Was für ein Film läuft denn im Regina Palast?

*B:* _____

*A:* Hier ist die Zeitung. Da stehen alle Filme.

*B:* _____

*A:* Von dem Film habe ich noch nichts gehört.

*B:* _____

*A:* Um halb fünf und um sieben.

**B:** _____

**A:** Treffen wir uns zehn vor sieben vor dem Regina Palast!

**B:** _____

***

**C:** _____

**D:** Zum Schultanz? Bestimmt.

**C:** _____

**D:** Das macht doch nichts. Du brauchst keine formelle Kleidung.

**C:** _____

**D:** Unser Lehrer hat gesagt, wir müssen keine elegante Kleidung anhaben.

**C:** _____

**D:** Ich weiß noch nicht. Vielleicht mit... (Name)

**C:** _____

**D:** Kannst du mir morgen sagen, ob du zum Tanz gehst?

**C:** _____

## 13 Wie heißen die fünf Nachbarländer der Schweiz (1-5) und die fünf Städte (A-E) in der Schweiz?

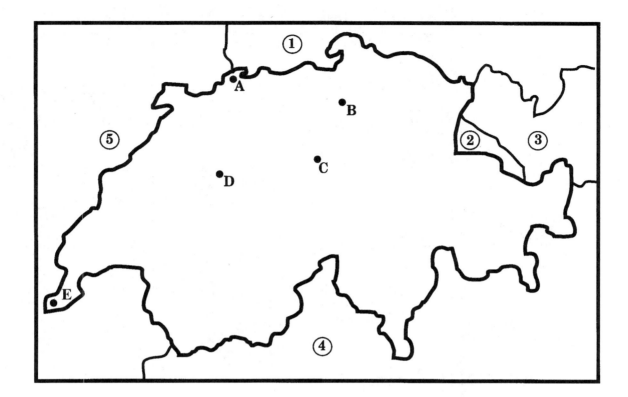

1. _____

2. _____

3. _____

4. _____

5. _____

A. _____

B. _____

C. _____

D. _____

E. _____

**Kreuzworträtsel (Note: Ä = AE, Ö = OE, Ü = UE)**

## WAAGERECHT

3. Zug, eine kleine Stadt, liegt nicht weit von Luzern ___.

5. Die Musik stört Simones ___ nicht.

6. Der größte Teil der Schweiz liegt in den ___.

8. Frau Kundmüller spielt eine CD mit moderner ___.

10. Sie ___ den ersten Teil.

14. Die Nationalfahne der Schweiz ist ___ und hat ein weißes Kreuz.

16. Manche Schüler sind ___, andere sind Fortgeschrittene.

17. Simone ruft ihre Freundinnen ___.

18. Alle drei ___ eine Mozart Serenade.

19. Gabriella und Daniela wohnen in ___, einer Stadt in der Schweiz.

## SENKRECHT

1. Katja bringt ihre ___.

2. Nadines ___ ist neu.

4. Die neusten ___ sind auf einer Tafel im Tanzstudio.

7. Frau Kundmüller ist die ___ im Tanzstudio.

9. Katja und Nadine ___ an der Tür.

11. ___ ist die Hauptstadt der Schweiz.

12. In einem ___ können sie sehen, wie sie tanzen.

13. ___ ist die größte Stadt der Schweiz.

15. Während alle ___, sagt ihnen die Lehrerin, was sie machen sollen.

**15** ***Was weißt du?*** **Fill in the correct information based on the content of this chapter. Write each missing item in capital letters. The first letters, when read in sequence, spell a key word in this chapter. (Note: Ü = UE, ß = SS)**

1. Luzern liegt in der _____ der Schweiz.

2. Frau Kundmüllers Tanzstunde beginnt um sechs _____.

3. Gabriella und Daniela fahren mit der _____ in die Stadtmitte.

4. Im Süden von der Schweiz liegt das Nachbarland _____.

5. Simones Vater gibt den drei Mädchen _____. Er schmeckt sehr gut.

6. Simone sagt von ihrem Vater: „Er hat unsere Musik _____ sehr gern."

7. Die _____ von der Schweiz ist rot und hat ein weißes Kreuz in der Mitte.

8. _____, Nadine und Katja machen Musik.

9. Der größte _____ der Schweiz liegt in den Bergen.

10. Der _____ ist der längste Fluss in der Schweiz.

11. _____ macht den Meister!

12. _____ hat „Eine kleine Nachtmusik" komponiert.

13. Die Schweiz hat mehr als sechs Millionen _____.

14. _____ hat eine neue Flöte.

15. Einmal die Woche gehen Daniela und Gabriella zu Frau Kundmüllers _____.

16. Die drei Mädchen üben „_____ kleine Nachtmusik".